Avery

Volume 2

Modules 10–20

ISBN   978-0-358-00230-7

5 6 7 8 9 10   0868   58 27 26 25 24 23 22 21

4500821037   C D E F G

Dear Students and Families,

Welcome to *Into Math, Grade 5!* In this program, you will develop skills and make sense of mathematics by solving real-world problems, using hands-on tools and strategies, and collaborating with your classmates.

With the support of your teacher and by engaging with meaningful practice, you will learn to persevere when solving problems. *Into Math* will not only help you deepen your understanding of mathematics, but also build your confidence as a learner of mathematics.

Even more exciting, you will write all your ideas and solutions right in your book. In your *Into Math* book, writing and drawing on the pages will help you think deeply about what you are learning, help you truly understand math, and most important, you will become a confident user of mathematics!

Sincerely,
The Authors

Authors

Edward B. Burger, PhD
President, Southwestern University
Georgetown, Texas

Matthew R. Larson, PhD
Past-President, National Council
of Teachers of Mathematics
Lincoln Public Schools
Lincoln, Nebraska

Juli K. Dixon, PhD
Professor, Mathematics Education
University of Central Florida
Orlando, Florida

Steven J. Leinwand
Principal Research Analyst
American Institutes for Research
Washington, DC

Timothy D. Kanold, PhD
Mathematics Educator
Chicago, Illinois

Jennifer Lempp
Educational Consultant
Alexandria, Virginia

Consultants

English Language Development Consultant

Harold Asturias
Director, Center for Mathematics
Excellence and Equity
Lawrence Hall of Science, University of California
Berkeley, California

Program Consultant

David Dockterman, EdD
Lecturer, Harvard Graduate School of Education
Cambridge, Massachusetts

Blended Learning Consultant

Weston Kieschnick
Senior Fellow
International Center for Leadership in Education
Littleton, Colorado

STEM Consultants

Michael A. DiSpezio
Global Educator
North Falmouth, Massachusetts

Marjorie Frank
Science Writer and
Content-Area Reading Specialist
Brooklyn, New York

Bernadine Okoro
Access and Equity and
STEM Learning Advocate and Consultant
Washington, DC

Cary I. Sneider, PhD
Associate Research Professor
Portland State University
Portland, Oregon

Unit 4

Divide Fractions and Convert Customary Units

○ **Build Understanding**   ○ **Connect Concepts and Skills**   ○ **Apply and Practice**

MODULE 11 Divide with Whole Numbers and Unit Fractions

MODULE 12 Customary Measurement

Unit 5

Add and Subtract Decimals

Build Understanding ⬤ Connect Concepts and Skills ⬤ Apply and Practice

© Houghton Mifflin Harcourt Publishing Company

⬤ Build Understanding   ⬤ Connect Concepts and Skills   ⬤ Apply and Practice

MODULE 18 Customary and Metric Measurement

MILK
1 gallon

Build Understanding   Connect Concepts and Skills   Apply and Practice

MODULE 20 Classify Two-Dimensional Figures

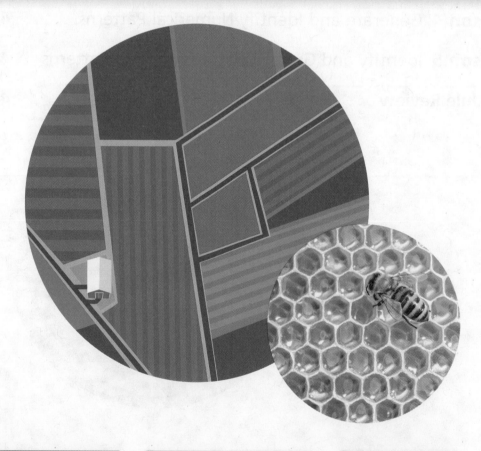

Build Understanding   Connect Concepts and Skills   Apply and Practice

Unit 4

Divide Fractions and Convert Customary Units

Astrophysicist

Astrophysicists use mathematics to explain their theories about the life cycles of galaxies, stars, and planets. Stephen Hawking was one of the world's most renowned astrophysicists.

Astrophysicists at NASA try to answer: How does the universe work? How did we get here? Are we alone? Astrophysicists analyze data and develop models. They have to persevere when they get stuck trying to make a good model.

Since 300 BC, astrophysicists have observed how the sun and stars move. They used this data to model our solar system. The first models did not explain all the data, so they persevered until the 1600s, when they made a model that worked.

STEM Task:

Galileo observed that Venus has phases and used this data to support the model of the solar system. Like Venus, our moon has phases. Research the phases of the moon and select one to focus on. What fraction of a month is this phase visible? Share your data with a partner. Write one question an astrophysicist might ask about the solar system based on this data.

Learning Mindset
Perseverance Getting Unstuck

Solving problems takes time. It often requires trying different strategies. Sometimes a small, unseen error can get you stuck. Slow down. Work the problem backwards. Check your work. There are times you might need help getting unstuck, so one of your strategies might be to ask for help. But don't give up too soon! Mathematicians and scientists sometimes take years to solve problems. One man took 14 years to find a prime number that has over 23 million digits!

Reflect

Q Think about a time you were working on a math problem and you got stuck. Was your strategy wrong or did you make an error executing the strategy? How did you get unstuck?

Q In the STEM Task, were your research strategies effective?

10 Understand Division with Whole Numbers and Unit Fractions

What is the secret number?

- Follow the steps to find the number of words in the Constitution of the United States of America, including all 27 amendments.

  A. Complete each equation to represent the shaded part of each fraction strip.

  | $\frac{1}{10}$ | $\frac{1}{10}$ | $\frac{1}{10}$ | $\frac{1}{10}$ | $\frac{1}{10}$ | $\frac{1}{10}$ | $\frac{1}{10}$ | $\frac{1}{10}$ | $\frac{1}{10}$ | $\frac{1}{10}$ |

  _____ × $\dfrac{1}{\boxed{}}$ = _____

  | $\frac{1}{6}$ | $\frac{1}{6}$ | $\frac{1}{6}$ | $\frac{1}{6}$ | $\frac{1}{6}$ | $\frac{1}{6}$ |

  _____ × $\dfrac{1}{\boxed{}}$ = _____

  | $\frac{1}{12}$ | $\frac{1}{12}$ | $\frac{1}{12}$ | $\frac{1}{12}$ | $\frac{1}{12}$ | $\frac{1}{12}$ | $\frac{1}{12}$ | $\frac{1}{12}$ | $\frac{1}{12}$ | $\frac{1}{12}$ | $\frac{1}{12}$ | $\frac{1}{12}$ |

  _____ × $\dfrac{1}{\boxed{}}$ = _____

  | $\frac{1}{5}$ | $\frac{1}{5}$ | $\frac{1}{5}$ | $\frac{1}{5}$ | $\frac{1}{5}$ |

  _____ × $\dfrac{1}{\boxed{}}$ = _____

  B. Write a 4-digit number using the whole-number factors from each equation. Write the factors in the same order as they appear.

The Constitution has _____ words.

 Turn and Talk

- Describe how to find the product $3 \times \frac{1}{8}$ without using a picture or repeated addition.

Are You Ready?

Complete these problems to review prior concepts and skills you will need for this module.

Represent Division

Complete the table. Use counters to help.

	Counters	Number of Equal Groups	Number in Each Group
1	30	6	
2	28		4
3	16	8	
4	27		3

Relate Multiplication and Division

Write the related facts for each set.

5 6, 7, 42　　　　6 3, 8, 24　　　　7 2, 9, 18

_____ ÷ _____ = _____　　_____ ÷ _____ = _____　　_____ ÷ _____ = _____

_____ × _____ = _____　　_____ × _____ = _____　　_____ × _____ = _____

_____ ÷ _____ = _____　　_____ ÷ _____ = _____　　_____ ÷ _____ = _____

_____ × _____ = _____　　_____ × _____ = _____　　_____ × _____ = _____

Equivalent Fractions

Write an equivalent fraction.

8 $\frac{16}{48}$ = _____　　　9 $\frac{6}{7}$ = _____　　　10 $\frac{5}{13}$ = _____

11 $\frac{16}{32}$ = _____　　12 $\frac{14}{18}$ = _____　　13 $\frac{55}{66}$ = _____

Name

Interpret a Fraction as Division

(I Can) interpret fractions as representing division of whole numbers.

Spark Your Learning

An elementary school receives 5 boxes of minerals for its earth science classes. The 6 science teachers at the school share the boxes equally for their classes. What fraction of a box will each teacher receive?

Turn and Talk What would happen if the school had received 8 boxes or 4 boxes? Describe how to determine the fraction of a box each teacher would get for different numbers of boxes.

Build Understanding

1 Five students in the science club prepare 4 circuit boards for a small satellite called a CubeSat. If they share the work equally, how many circuit boards does each student prepare?

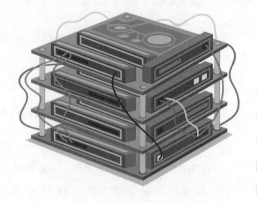

A. Draw to represent the situation.

B. How does your drawing represent the situation?

_____

_____

_____

C. What does the expression 4 ÷ 5 model?

_____

D. Write a division equation to model the situation.

_____

E. What does your quotient represent?

_____

_____

> **Connect to Vocabulary**
>
> In an earlier lesson, you divided whole-number **dividends** by 2-digit **divisors** to find **quotients**.

 Turn and Talk In Part D, you wrote a division equation to model the situation. How does the equation show the relationship between division and a fraction?

2 Two scientists develop a new substance in a laboratory. They make a total of 5 milliliters. If the substance is shared equally, how many milliliters does each scientist get?

A. Draw to represent the situation.

B. How does your visual model represent the dividend, the divisor, and the quotient of a division equation that models this situation?

_____

_____

C. What is the size of each group and what does it mean for

this situation? _____

D. What division expression models the situation? _____

E. Divide the expression you wrote in Part D and compare it to

your answer in Part C. _____

 Turn and Talk Denisa divides the expression in Part D and gets $\frac{5}{2}$, while Cal divides and gets $2\frac{1}{2}$. Who is correct and why? How do you know whether the answers are reasonable?

• •

Check Understanding Math Board

Represent the situation with an equation or visual model and solve.

1 Three runners in a relay race share the 8-mile distance equally. How many miles does each runner travel?

_____

On Your Own

MP **Model with Mathematics** **Model the situation with a division equation and find the quotient.**

2 Five friends share 6 small bags of popcorn. If they share the popcorn equally, how many bags of popcorn does each friend receive?

3 Twelve friends shovel snow from 8 identical driveways. If they share the work evenly, what part of a driveway does each friend shovel?

4 **Open Ended** Describe a situation that can be modeled by $3 \div 5$. Then draw a visual model to represent the situation and use it to find the quotient.

5 An audio engineer divides 9 feet of cable into 2 equal sections to connect a pair of speakers. How long is each section of cable?

6 **MP** **Reason** Two groups of people sit at different tables in a restaurant. The first group of 6 people orders three small pizzas. The second group of 8 people orders four small pizzas. The people at each table share their pizzas equally. How does the amount of pizza per person at each table compare? Explain.

 I'm in a Learning Mindset!

What strategies can I use to model a division situation?

Represent and Find the Size of Equal Parts

(I Can) divide a unit fraction by a whole number using a visual fraction model.

Spark Your Learning

A recreation center has a batting cage with a machine that pitches balls to the batter. Five friends sign up for a $\frac{1}{2}$ hour of time in the batting cage. If they share the $\frac{1}{2}$ hour equally, how much of a whole hour will each friend get in the batting cage? Explain.

Each friend will get _____ hour in the batting cage.

  Turn and Talk How would your answer change if the friends had signed up for $\frac{1}{4}$ hour?

Build Understanding

1 The distance around the track at the recreation center is $\frac{1}{4}$ mile. Maeda, Will, and Holly plan to divide the distance evenly to practice sprints. What distance does each person run?

Write an expression and draw a visual model to represent the situation.

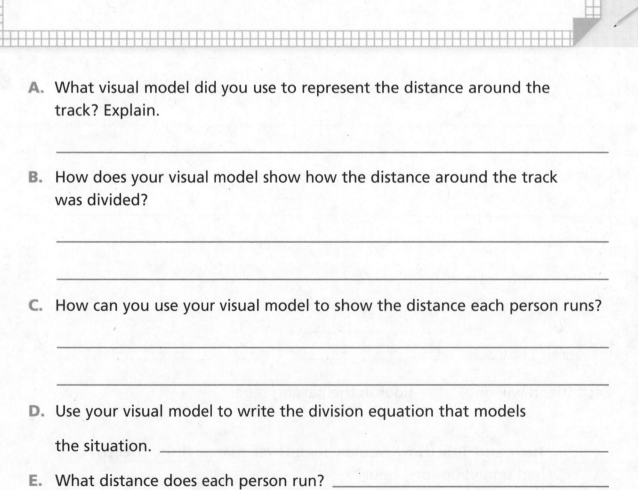

A. What visual model did you use to represent the distance around the track? Explain.

_____

B. How does your visual model show how the distance around the track was divided?

_____

_____

C. How can you use your visual model to show the distance each person runs?

_____

_____

D. Use your visual model to write the division equation that models

the situation. _____

E. What distance does each person run? _____

Step It Out

2 One third of the recreation center pool is reserved for lap swimming. If this part of the pool is divided equally for 2 swimmers, what fraction of the pool will each swimmer have?

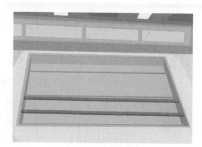

A. Model the situation with an expression. _____

B. Place a unit fraction strip under a 1-whole strip to show the dividend. Draw the model.

C. Place fraction strips, all with the same denominator, that fit exactly under the unit fraction strip. Then draw the model.

D. What fraction of the pool will each swimmer have? Write a division equation to model the situation.

_____

Turn and Talk Why do you need to use fraction strips with the same denominator to show how much of the pool each swimmer will have?

Check Understanding [Math Board]

1 One fourth of a cheese wheel is divided equally among 5 people at a picnic. How much of a whole wheel of cheese

will each person get? _____

Draw fraction strips to find the quotient.

2 $\frac{1}{6} \div 2 =$ _____

3 $\frac{1}{2} \div 3 =$ _____

4 $\frac{1}{3} \div 4 =$ _____

On Your Own

5 (MP) **Use Tools** A cement truck carries $\frac{1}{5}$ ton of concrete. The truck will pour an equal amount of concrete for each of two houses.

- Draw a visual model to represent the problem.

- Write a division equation to model this situation.

  _____

- Explain what the quotient means in this situation.

  _____

Divide. Use a visual model to find the quotient.

6 $\frac{1}{3} \div 2 =$ _____

7 _____ $= \frac{1}{8} \div 2$

8 _____ $= \frac{1}{5} \div 4$

9 $\frac{1}{4} \div 4 =$ _____

10 _____ $= \frac{1}{6} \div 3$

11 $\frac{1}{10} \div 2 =$ _____

12 (MP) **Use Structure** Gerardo divides $\frac{1}{2}$ by 2, and then divides the quotient by 2 again. Draw a circle to represent one whole. Then use it to explain how Gerardo's work is similar to dividing $\frac{1}{2}$ by 4.

_____

_____

_____

_____

⬡ I'm in a Learning Mindset!

How do I stay focused when dividing unit fractions by whole numbers?

_____

© Houghton Mifflin Harcourt Publishing Company • Image Credit: © Christina Richards/Shutterstock

Name

Use Representations of Division of Unit Fractions by Whole Numbers

I Can create a story context and use a visual fraction model to interpret the division of a unit fraction by a whole number.

Spark Your Learning

Darren thinks about how he can use division of unit fractions by whole numbers in his cooking class. He considers the expression $\frac{1}{2} \div 8$. What word problem can be written for $\frac{1}{2} \div 8$? Draw a visual model to show the quotient, and then explain what it represents.

SMALL GROUPS

Turn and Talk When dividing a fraction by a whole number, what do you notice about the values of the dividend and the quotient? Explain how they compare.

Build Understanding

1 Darren considers situations in which a fractional quantity is divided into equal groups. Darren thinks about the expression $\frac{1}{4} \div 2$.

A. Describe a situation in which $\frac{1}{4}$ of an item can be divided into 2 equal parts. How do the quantities represent the dividend, the divisor, and the quotient?

_____

_____

_____

B. What word problem can you write that can be modeled by $\frac{1}{4} \div 2$, and includes a question about the size of each part?

_____

_____

Draw a visual model to show the quotient.

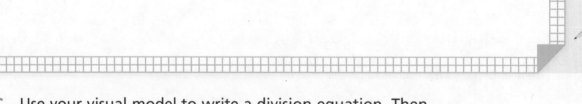

C. Use your visual model to write a division equation. Then explain what the quotient represents.

_____

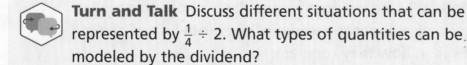
Turn and Talk Discuss different situations that can be represented by $\frac{1}{4} \div 2$. What types of quantities can be modeled by the dividend?

2 Write and solve a word problem that can be modeled by the expression $\frac{1}{2} \div 6$. Draw a visual model to show the quotient, and then explain what it represents.

A. What word problem can you write that can be modeled by $\frac{1}{2} \div 6$?

_____

_____

_____

_____

Draw a visual model to show the quotient.

B. Describe the size of each part and what it represents.

_____

C. Solve your word problem. What does the quotient represent?

_____

_____

 Turn and Talk How did you decide the type of visual model to use for your problem? Explain.

Step It Out

3 Look at the visual model.

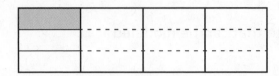

A. Write a division word problem that can be represented by the visual model.

_____

_____

_____

B. Write a division equation to model your problem. Then solve the problem.

_____

Check Understanding

1 Amy writes a word problem that can be modeled by the expression $\frac{1}{4} \div 5$. Complete her word problem.

There are _____ truck(s) that need to share the total amount of recycled plastic bottles equally. If there is a

collection of _____ ton of plastic bottles, then how much does each truck carry?

2 A doctor has $\frac{1}{2}$ hour to see 3 patients. If the doctor divides the time equally among the patients, how much time will be spent with each patient? Draw a visual model to represent the problem.

_____

On Your Own

3 Write a word problem that involves a plot of land and a number of different crops that can be modeled by the expression $\frac{1}{2} \div 5$.

_____

_____

- Will the quotient be less than $\frac{1}{2}$ or greater than $\frac{1}{2}$? Justify your thinking.

_____

_____

4 (MP) **Use Tools** Write a word problem for the expression $\frac{1}{5} \div 4$. Then draw a visual model and solve your problem.

_____

_____

5 (MP) **Attend to Precision** Margie writes a word problem for the expression $\frac{1}{3} \div 6$: "A bottle of mouthwash is $\frac{1}{3}$ empty. If the remaining amount is divided equally over 6 weeks, what fraction of the bottle is used each week?"

- What mistake did she make in her problem?

_____

_____

- Correct her word problem. Then find the answer using a visual model.

_____

_____

_____

On Your Own

6 (MP) **Model with Mathematics** Write a division word problem that can be represented by the visual model. Then write a division equation and solve your problem.

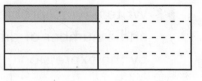

_____

_____

_____

7 **Open Ended** Consider the expression $\frac{1}{5} \div 3$.

- Write two different word problems that can be represented by this expression.

_____

_____

_____

_____

- Draw a visual model to represent the problems and then solve.

- What does the quotient represent in each problem?

_____

 I'm in a Learning Mindset!

How can I work with others to write word problems?

_____

Name _____

Represent and Find the Number of Equal-Sized Parts

(**I Can**) divide a whole number by a unit fraction using a visual fraction model.

Spark Your Learning

A nature preserve is 5 miles wide. A ranger divides the entire preserve into $\frac{1}{3}$-mile wide sections for different tours. How many sections does the nature preserve have for different tours?

Justify your answer.

SMALL GROUPS

$\frac{1}{2}$

Turn and Talk What if the ranger chose to divide the preserve into sections that were $\frac{1}{6}$-mile wide? How would your answer change?

Build Understanding

1 The nature preserve has a 3-mile long trail for birdwatchers. The ranger divides the trail into $\frac{1}{2}$-mile sections and names each section after a different bird. How many of these sections does the trail have?

A. Complete to describe the situation and model it with an expression.

The trail is _____ miles long and is divided

into _____-mile sections. This can be modeled

by the expression _____.

B. Represent the situation with the number line.

0

- How is the dividend represented on the number line?

  _____

- How is the divisor represented on the number line?

  _____

- How is the quotient represented on the number line?

  _____

C. What division equation can you write? Interpret your answer in this situation.

_____

_____

 Turn and Talk How can you find out how many $\frac{1}{2}$-mile sections are in 9 miles?

Step It Out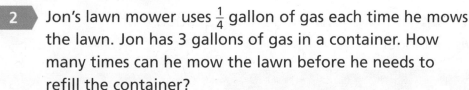

2 Jon's lawn mower uses $\frac{1}{4}$ gallon of gas each time he mows the lawn. Jon has 3 gallons of gas in a container. How many times can he mow the lawn before he needs to refill the container?

A. Represent the amount of gas in the container. Draw rectangles to show each gallon.

B. Divide each rectangle from Part A into fourths to represent the amount of gas needed to mow the lawn.

C. Count the number of equal parts in the smaller rectangles to find the quotient. Write a division equation to model the problem and explain what the quotient means in this situation.

_____

_____

_____

Check Understanding

Draw a visual model to solve the problem, and then write a division equation.

1 Tim serves $\frac{1}{5}$ pound of cat food each day from a 2-pound bag. How many days will this bag last?

On Your Own

2 (MP) **Model with Mathematics** Write a division equation that represents the visual model.

1				1			
$\frac{1}{4}$	$\frac{1}{4}$	$\frac{1}{4}$	$\frac{1}{4}$	$\frac{1}{4}$	$\frac{1}{4}$	$\frac{1}{4}$	$\frac{1}{4}$

_____

3 Draw a visual model to represent $2 \div \frac{1}{6}$. Then find the quotient.

$2 \div \frac{1}{6} =$ _____

4 Tyra has 4 liters of distilled water for a chemistry experiment. This is $\frac{1}{5}$ of the amount she needs. How much distilled water

does she need? _____

5 (MP) **Model with Mathematics** Draw visual models to complete the equations.

- $3 \div \frac{1}{2} =$ _____

- $2 \div \frac{1}{3} =$ _____

- How are the two equations the same? Explain your thinking.

_____

_____

 # I'm in a **Learning Mindset!**

How is using visual models effective in solving a problem?

_____

© Houghton Mifflin Harcourt Publishing Company

Name

Use Representations of Division of Whole Numbers by Unit Fractions

(I Can) create a story context and use a visual fraction model to interpret the division of a whole number by a unit fraction.

Spark Your Learning

Karlus has a honey jar. Write a word problem about the honey jar that can be modeled by the expression $5 \div \frac{1}{2}$. How can a visual model be used to solve the problem?

Draw a visual model. Explain your thinking.

 Turn and Talk How does dividing a whole number by a unit fraction differ from dividing a unit fraction by a whole number?

Build Understanding

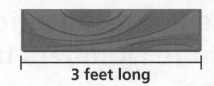

3 feet long

1 Elsa uses the plank of wood to make a craft
project at the community center.

A. What word problem can you write about the plank of wood
that can be modeled by $3 \div \frac{1}{4}$?

_____

_____

B. How do the quantities represent the dividend, the divisor,
and the quotient?

_____

_____

_____

C. Draw a visual model to show the quotient.

D. Use your visual model to write a division equation. Then
write a statement to interpret the quotient for this situation.

_____

_____

 Turn and Talk Elsa writes this word problem for $3 \div \frac{1}{2}$:
"Mr. Grant tutors 3 students after school. He divides his time
among the students equally. If the tutoring session lasts $\frac{1}{2}$
hour, how long will he spend with each student?" Is Elsa's
problem modeled by $3 \div \frac{1}{2}$? Explain.

2 Lien prepares some appetizers for a party. Write a word problem about the appetizers that can be modeled by the expression $2 \div \frac{1}{8}$. Use a visual model to help solve the problem.

A. What word problem models the expression and includes a question about the number of equal parts?

_____

_____

B. Which quantities in the story represent the dividend, the divisor, and the quotient?

_____

_____

Draw a visual model to show the quotient.

C. Describe the number of equal parts in your visual model and what they represent.

_____

D. Use your work to write a division equation. Then write a statement to interpret the quotient for this situation.

_____

 Turn and Talk How would your quotient have changed if you were dividing by $\frac{1}{4}$ instead of $\frac{1}{8}$? Explain.

Step It Out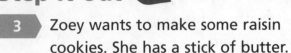

3 ▸ Zoey wants to make some raisin cookies. She has a stick of butter.

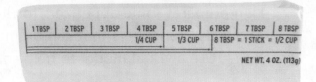

1 TBSP	2 TBSP	3 TBSP	4 TBSP	5 TBSP	6 TBSP	7 TBSP	8 TBSP
			1/4 CUP	1/3 CUP		8 TBSP = 1 STICK = 1/2 CUP	

NET WT. 4 OZ. (113g)

A. Write a word problem, using the stick of butter, that can be modeled by the expression $8 \div \frac{1}{3}$.

_____

_____

_____

B. Draw a visual model to show the quotient.

C. Interpret the quotient in the context of your word problem.

_____

● ●

Check Understanding [Math Board]

1 Rami buys some apples. Write a word problem that can be modeled by the expression $4 \div \frac{1}{6}$. Then draw a visual model and find the quotient.

_____

_____

Find the quotient.

2 $7 \div \frac{1}{3} =$ _____

3 $9 \div \frac{1}{5} =$ _____

On Your Own

4 (MP) **Model with Mathematics** Write a word problem about pizza that can be modeled by the expression $7 \div \frac{1}{8}$.

- Write a word problem for the division expression.

  _____

  _____

- Draw a visual model to show the quotient.

- Interpret the quotient in the context of your word problem.

  _____

Find the quotient.

5 $10 \div \frac{1}{2} =$ _____   **6** $6 \div \frac{1}{3} =$ _____   **7** $3 \div \frac{1}{12} =$ _____

8 (MP) **Use Tools** There are 5 sandwiches on a platter. One serving is $\frac{1}{4}$ of a sandwich. How many servings are there? Draw a visual model to find the quotient.

_____

9 (MP) **Attend to Precision** Ian writes a word problem that can be modeled by the expression $2 \div \frac{1}{3}$.

Mycaela has 2 jars of peanut butter. She needs $\frac{1}{3}$ cup for one batch of oatmeal bites. How many batches of oatmeal bites can she make?

Does the word problem match the division expression? Explain.

_____

_____

On Your Own

10 (MP) **Use Repeated Reasoning** Rami divides a whole number by a unit fraction, and then divides the quotient by another unit fraction. Is the second quotient less than or greater than the original whole number? Explain.

_____

_____

_____

_____

11 **Open Ended** Mae uses the expression $5 \div \frac{1}{6}$ to solve a problem.

- Write a word problem that can be modeled by the expression.

_____

_____

- Draw a visual representation to show the quotient.

- Write an equation to model the problem. Interpret the quotient for the situation.

_____

 I'm in a Learning Mindset!

How does explaining my strategy help me write division word problems and model the quotient?

_____

Vocabulary

Choose the correct term from the vocabulary box to complete the sentence.

Vocabulary

dividend
divisor
quotient
remainder

1 In the equation $\frac{1}{2} \div 3 = \frac{1}{6}$, $\frac{1}{6}$ is the _____.

2 In the equation $4 \div \frac{1}{3} = 12$, $\frac{1}{3}$ is the _____.

3 In the equation $\frac{1}{4} \div 2 = \frac{1}{8}$, $\frac{1}{4}$ is the _____.

Concepts and Skills

4 Carly has 28 fluid ounces of juice. She divides the juice equally into 5 glasses. How many fluid ounces are in each glass? Model the situation with a division equation and find the quotient.

_____

5 Which expression is equivalent to $\frac{7}{10}$?

Ⓐ 7 – 10

Ⓒ 7 ÷ 10

Ⓑ 10 – 7

Ⓓ 10 ÷ 7

6 (MP) **Use Tools** Write and solve a word problem that can be modeled by the expression $\frac{1}{2} \div 6$. Name the strategy or tool you will use to solve the problem, explain your choice, and then find the answer.

_____

_____

_____

_____

_____

7 Shannon has 4 quarts of soup. If each serving of soup is $\frac{1}{4}$ quart, how many servings of soup does she have? Write a division equation to model the situation.

_____

8 What is the quotient $\frac{1}{6} \div 3$? Draw a visual model to represent the expression and find the quotient.

_____

9 Manny divides $\frac{1}{3}$ pound of peanuts equally into 2 bags. How many pounds of peanuts are in each bag?

Ⓐ $1\frac{2}{3}$ pounds   Ⓒ $\frac{1}{3}$ pound

Ⓑ $\frac{2}{3}$ pound   Ⓓ $\frac{1}{6}$ pound

10 Select all the expressions equivalent to 12.

Ⓐ $3 \div \frac{1}{4}$

Ⓑ $2 \div \frac{1}{6}$

Ⓒ $\frac{1}{6} \div 2$

Ⓓ $4 \div \frac{1}{3}$

Ⓔ $\frac{1}{2} \div 6$

11 Write and solve a word problem that can be modeled by the expression $6 \div \frac{1}{8}$.

_____

_____

_____

Divide with Whole Numbers and Unit Fractions

Which cup should I use?

- You want to fill the large container so that it has more than 5 cups of water but less than $5\frac{1}{3}$ cups of water.

- You can choose only one of the three glasses to fill the container and each glass must be full each time.

Holds
$5\frac{1}{3}$ cups

$\frac{7}{8}$ cup

$\frac{2}{3}$ cup

$\frac{1}{2}$ cup

- You can fill and empty each glass only 8 times. Complete the table.

NUMBER OF CUPS OF WATER IN LARGE CONTAINER					
Glass holds	4 fills	5 fills	6 fills	7 fills	8 fills
$\frac{1}{2}$ c	$\frac{4}{2} = 2$				
$\frac{7}{8}$ c	$\frac{28}{8} = 3\frac{4}{8}$				
$\frac{2}{3}$ c	$\frac{8}{3} = 2\frac{2}{3}$				

- Which glass would you choose? How many times would you need to fill the glass?

_____

 Turn and Talk

- How did you solve the problem?

Are You Ready?

Complete these problems to review prior concepts and skills
you will need for this module.

Part of a Whole

Write the fraction that names the equal part. Then write a fraction to name the
shaded part of the whole.

1 Each equal part is $\dfrac{\square}{\square}$. $\dfrac{\square}{\square}$ is shaded.

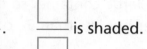

2 Each equal part is $\dfrac{\square}{\square}$. $\dfrac{\square}{\square}$ is shaded.

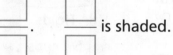

Add Fractions

Find the sum.

3 $\dfrac{1}{8} + \dfrac{1}{8} =$ _____

4 $\dfrac{1}{9} + \dfrac{1}{9} + \dfrac{1}{9} + \dfrac{1}{9} + \dfrac{1}{9} =$ _____

5 $\dfrac{1}{6} + \dfrac{1}{6} + \dfrac{4}{6} =$ _____

6 $\dfrac{1}{5} + \dfrac{1}{5} + \dfrac{1}{5} + \dfrac{1}{5} =$ _____

Relate Multiplication and Division

Write the related facts for each set.

7 4, 5, 20 **8** 3, 9, 27 **9** 7, 8, 56

____ ÷ ____ = ____   ____ ÷ ____ = ____   ____ ÷ ____ = ____

____ × ____ = ____   ____ × ____ = ____   ____ × ____ = ____

____ ÷ ____ = ____   ____ ÷ ____ = ____   ____ ÷ ____ = ____

____ × ____ = ____   ____ × ____ = ____   ____ × ____ = ____

Name

Relate Multiplication and Division of Fractions

(I Can) divide a whole number by a unit fraction or a unit fraction by a whole number using a related multiplication equation.

Spark Your Learning

Josiah buys six packages of ground beef. How many $\frac{1}{4}$-pound hamburgers can Josiah make from the six packages?

A classmate began solving this problem by using a visual fraction model. How can you complete the model and use it to solve the problem?

 Turn and Talk How can you model this problem with a division equation? How can you model this problem with a multiplication equation?

Build Understanding

1 Josiah has 3 pounds of potato salad for his cookout. He divides the potato salad into $\frac{1}{4}$-pound servings. How many $\frac{1}{4}$-pound servings does Josiah have?

A. Write an equation to model the situation. _____

Represent the equation by drawing rectangles as a visual model.

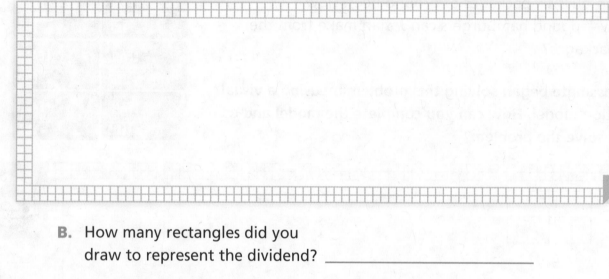

B. How many rectangles did you draw to represent the dividend? _____

C. How did you represent the divisor in your visual fraction model?

_____

D. How does your visual fraction model represent the quotient?

_____

E. How many $\frac{1}{4}$-pound servings of potato salad does Josiah have? _____

F. How can you use a multiplication equation to represent your visual fraction model?

$3 \div \frac{1}{4} =$ _____

 Turn and Talk For Part E, how can you use the relationship between multiplication and division to show that your answer is correct?

Step It Out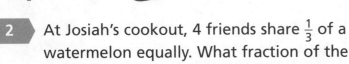

2 At Josiah's cookout, 4 friends share $\frac{1}{3}$ of a watermelon equally. What fraction of the whole watermelon does each friend get?

A. Write an equation to represent the problem.

_____

B. Draw a visual model to represent the equation.

- The rectangle represents the whole watermelon. Divide the rectangle to represent the dividend.

- Divide the dividend to represent the divisor.

- Divide the other sections in the same way.

- Shade the part that each friend gets.

C. What fraction of the whole watermelon does each friend get? _____

D. What related multiplication equation can you write to represent the problem? Explain.

_____

_____

Check Understanding [Math Board]

Represent the situation with a visual model. Then write a division equation and a related multiplication equation.

1 Josiah serves $\frac{1}{2}$ pound of macaroni salad equally to 6 guests. What fraction of a pound does each guest get?

_____

On Your Own

2 The container of milk is divided equally into 8 glasses. How much milk should be poured into each glass?

_____

Divide. Write a related multiplication equation to solve.

3 $8 \div \frac{1}{12} = n$

_____

4 $n = 4 \div \frac{1}{8}$

_____

5 $\frac{1}{10} \div 3 = n$

_____

6 $6 \div \frac{1}{5} = n$

_____

7 $n = \frac{1}{5} \div 6$

_____

8 $n = \frac{1}{9} \div 7$

_____

9 **(MP) Critique Reasoning** Lulu says that when you divide any whole number by a unit fraction, the quotient is always another whole number that is less than the dividend. Is Lulu correct? Explain.

_____

_____

10 **(MP) Use Tools** Four friends divide $\frac{1}{2}$ of an apple pie equally. What fraction of the pie does each friend get? Describe how you could divide a circle to find the answer.

_____

_____

 I'm in a Learning Mindset!

When I get stuck, how can I use different strategies to divide fractions?

_____

Name _____

Divide Whole Numbers by Unit Fractions

(I Can) represent division of a whole number by a unit fraction using visual fraction models and equations.

Step It Out

1 Cat and Ann complete a new obstacle course. The course is 2 miles long, and there is an obstacle every $\frac{1}{4}$ mile. How many obstacles are there?

A. Model the situation with an equation. Let p stand for the number of obstacles.

_____

B. Represent the division equation on the number line.

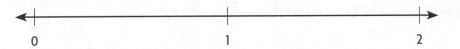

0   1   2

- How does the number line represent the dividend?

_____

_____

- Represent the divisor on the number line. Draw tick marks and label the fractions.

- Represent the quotient. Count the number of fourths there are in 2 wholes.

C. How many obstacles does the course have?

_____

 Turn and Talk When representing fractions on a number line, how is the number of tick marks between each whole number related to the fraction you are representing?

© Houghton Mifflin Harcourt Publishing Company

2 Cat and Ann practice the rope climb at the obstacle course. The rope is 3 yards long and there is a knot every $\frac{1}{3}$ yard. How many knots are there?

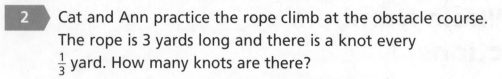

A. Model the situation with an equation. Let k represent the number of knots. _____

B. Use the number line to represent the division equation.

- Represent the dividend by drawing and labeling the tick marks.

- Represent the divisor by drawing and labeling the tick marks.

- Represent the quotient by counting.

C. How many knots are on the rope? _____

D. What related multiplication equation can you use to solve

the problem? Explain how you know. _____

_____

 Turn and Talk How are the dividend, the divisor, and the quotient represented on a number line to show division?

Check Understanding

Write a division equation to model the situation. Then complete the number line and write a related multiplication equation to solve the problem.

1 A walking trail is 4 miles long. There are benches along the trail every $\frac{1}{2}$ mile. How many benches are there?

_____

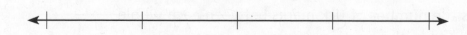

© Houghton Mifflin Harcourt Publishing Company

On Your Own

2 (MP) **Model with Mathematics** Duane and his family are playing a game. Duane scores 11 points. Each tile match is $\frac{1}{3}$ point. Model the situation with an equation. How many tile matches does Duane make?

_____

3 **Model with Mathematics** Mila swims 3 miles at the pool. She stops to take a break every $\frac{1}{2}$ mile. How many times does Mila stop to take a break?

- Model the situation with an equation.

_____

- Represent the dividend, divisor, and quotient on the number line.

<—————————————————————————————>

- How many times does Mila stop to take a break? Write a related multiplication equation to represent the number of times Mila stops to take a break.

_____

Divide. Write a related multiplication equation to solve.

4 $4 \div \frac{1}{5} = n$ **5** $n = 8 \div \frac{1}{3}$ **6** $4 \div \frac{1}{9} = n$

_____   _____   _____

7 An oceanic probe descends $\frac{1}{2}$ kilometer each minute. How many minutes will it take the probe to descend 10 kilometers into the deepest part of the ocean?

_____

On Your Own

8 Each bag of crackers in a box represents $\frac{1}{15}$ of the box. How many bags of crackers are in 3 boxes?

_____

9 (MP) **Construct Arguments** For what whole number value(s) of a is $17 \div \frac{1}{a}$ less than 17? Justify your reasoning.

_____

_____

10 (MP) **Model with Mathematics** Valerie has 6 feet of red ribbon and 25 feet of blue ribbon that she cuts into equal pieces.

- How many pieces of the red ribbon does she cut if each is $\frac{1}{12}$ foot long? Write a division equation and a related multiplication equation to solve.

_____

- How many pieces of the blue ribbon does she cut if each is $\frac{1}{3}$ foot long? Write a division equation and a related multiplication equation to solve.

_____

Divide. Write a related multiplication equation to solve.

11 $14 \div \frac{1}{3} = n$ **12** $n = 5 \div \frac{1}{16}$

_____   _____

13 **Open Ended** Maggie has a goal of jogging 100 miles. The distance she runs each day is the same unit fraction. What are some possible fractions of a mile she can run each day and the number of days it will take her to reach her goal? Explain how you found your answers.

_____

_____

_____

© Houghton Mifflin Harcourt Publishing Company

Name _____

Interpret and Solve Division of a Whole Number by a Unit Fraction

(I Can) create a story context for a given equation and use a visual fraction model to represent the quotient.

Step It Out

1 What problem can be solved by finding the number of $\frac{1}{4}$-size parts in 4 wholes?

A. What can be the 4 wholes? _____

B. What can be the $\frac{1}{4}$-size parts in a whole?

_____

_____

C. Write a problem that can be solved by finding the number of $\frac{1}{4}$-size parts in 4 wholes.

_____

_____

D. Use a visual fraction model to represent the problem.

E. What is the quotient, and what does it represent in the context of your problem? What equation can you write to model your problem?

_____

 Turn and Talk How would the problem change if the equation were $4 \div \frac{1}{8} = t$?

Step It Out

2 Write a word problem that can be modeled by $t = 5 \div \frac{1}{3}$. Then solve the problem using a visual fraction model.

A. Write a word problem that can be modeled by the division equation.

_____

_____

_____

B. Use a visual model to solve.

C. What is the quotient, and what does it represent in the context of your problem?

_____

 Turn and Talk What are some other word problems that can be modeled by $t = 5 \div \frac{1}{3}$?

Check Understanding

1 Write and solve a division word problem for the visual fraction model.

_____

_____

2 Write and solve a word problem that can be modeled by $r = 8 \div \frac{1}{10}$.

_____

_____

On Your Own

3 (MP) **Use Tools** Write and solve a division word problem for the visual model.

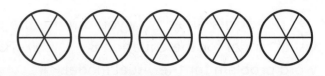

_____

_____

4 (MP) **Reason** Harry has two pounds of sculpting clay. He divides the clay into $\frac{1}{16}$-pound blocks. Can this situation be modeled by $16 \div \frac{1}{2} = b$ and $2 \div \frac{1}{16} = b$? Explain.

_____

_____

5 (MP) **Model with Mathematics** Write and solve a word problem that can be modeled by $k = 13 \div \frac{1}{10}$.

_____

_____

6 (MP) **Model with Mathematics** Use the visual model to write and solve a division word problem.

- Write a division equation for the visual model. _____

- Write a word problem that can be modeled by the equation.

_____

_____

_____

- Describe what the quotient means in the context of your problem.

_____

On Your Own

7 (MP) **Use Tools** Show how you can use the triangles to make a visual model for the equation $8 \div \frac{1}{2} = h$. Then write and solve a word problem for the visual model.

_____

_____

8 (MP) **Attend to Precision** Draw a visual model to represent $s = 4 \div \frac{1}{10}$.

- Write a word problem that can be represented by your visual model.

_____

_____

- Describe what the quotient means in the context of your problem.

_____

9 (MP) **Use Tools** Write a word problem that can be represented by $3 \div \frac{1}{6} = t$. Draw a visual model to help you solve the problem.

_____

_____

Name _____

Divide Unit Fractions by Whole Numbers

(I Can) represent division of a unit fraction by a whole number using visual fraction models and equations.

Step It Out

1 ▸ Darsha has 3 days to read $\frac{1}{2}$ of a book. She plans to read an equal amount each day. How much of the book will Darsha read each day?

A. Model the situation with an equation. Let t represent how much of the book Darsha will read each day.

_____

B. What part of the division equation represents the part of the book that Darsha has to read? _____

C. What part of the division equation represents the number of days that Darsha has to read the book? _____

D. Represent the situation with a visual fraction model.

E. What part of the whole book does each equal part represent? How much of the book does Darsha read each day?

_____

 Turn and Talk A student said that she could verify her answer by multiplying $\frac{1}{3} \times \frac{1}{2}$. Do you agree? Why or why not?

Step It Out

2 Darsha has $\frac{1}{3}$ of her math homework left to complete. If it takes her 4 minutes to finish it, how much of her math homework does Darsha complete each minute?

A. Write an equation that models the situation. _____

B. Represent the equation on the number line.

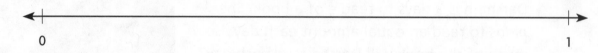

0   1

- What does the length from 0 to 1 on the number line

  represent? _____

- Draw tick marks to represent the dividend on the number line from 0 to 1.

- Which section of the number line represents

  the dividend? _____

- Shade in the section to represent the dividend.

- Draw tick marks to represent the divisor.

- How many equal lengths do you have? _____

- Repeat the division of equal lengths on the entire

  number line. How many are there? _____

- What does the size of each equal length represent?

  _____

- Circle the quotient on the number line.

C. How much of her homework does Darsha complete

each minute? _____

 Turn and Talk Why do you need to divide the whole number line into equal lengths and not just $\frac{1}{3}$ of it?

Check Understanding

1 Darsha writes $\frac{1}{4}$ of a report equally over 5 days. How much of the whole report does she write each day? Write an equation to model the situation. Represent the equation on the number line and circle the quotient.

0   1

_____

Divide. Write a related multiplication equation to solve.

2 $\frac{1}{6} \div 9 = n$ **3** $n = \frac{1}{10} \div 6$ **4** $\frac{1}{7} \div 4 = n$

_____   _____   _____

On Your Own

5 (MP) **Reason** Is 39 a reasonable answer for $\frac{1}{13} \div 3$? Explain.

_____

_____

Divide. Write a related multiplication equation to solve.

6 $\frac{1}{15} \div 5 = n$ **7** $n = \frac{1}{8} \div 12$ **8** $\frac{1}{20} \div 7 = n$

_____   _____   _____

9 **Open Ended** Use the number line to represent a division problem with a unit fraction divided by a whole number.

0   1

- Write an equation to represent the division problem. Then circle the quotient on the number line.

_____

On Your Own

10 (MP) **Model with Mathematics** Joshua has $\frac{1}{3}$ pound of fertilizer for 3 flower beds. If he puts an equal amount of fertilizer in each flower bed, how much fertilizer does he put in each bed? Write an equation to model the situation. Then represent the problem using a visual model.

11 **Open Ended** Greta solves a division problem in which the quotient is $\frac{1}{48}$. What are two possible equations that could have a quotient of $\frac{1}{48}$? Justify your answer.

12 (MP) **Use Structure** You divide $\frac{1}{8}$ by 4. In a number line representing this division:

- What would you label your large tick marks? Into how many smaller sections would you divide each equal length?

- What is the quotient? _____

13 (MP) **Use Tools** Kecia cuts a $\frac{1}{4}$-pound pepper into 6 equal-sized pieces. How much of one whole pound is each piece? Represent the problem on the number line.

0 ——————————————————————————————————— 1

Name _____

Interpret and Solve Division of a Unit Fraction by a Whole Number

(I Can) create a story context for a given equation and use a visual fraction model to represent the quotient.

Step It Out

1 Write a word problem that can be modeled by $p = \frac{1}{2} \div 4$. Then use a visual fraction model to solve the problem.

A. Write a word problem that can be modeled by the equation.

_____

_____

B. Represent your word problem with a rectangle.

- Divide the rectangle to represent the equation.

- Shade the part to represent the quotient.

C. Explain how you used the rectangle.

_____

_____

_____

_____

D. What fraction of your rectangle represents

the quotient? _____

E. Interpret the quotient in the context of your word problem.

_____

 Turn and Talk Why should you divide each half of the rectangle into 4 equal groups?

Step It Out

2 Write a word problem for the equation $t = \frac{1}{3} \div 2$. Then use a visual model to solve and represent the quotient.

A. Write a word problem that can be modeled by the equation.

_____

_____

B. Draw a visual model to represent the quotient.

C. Interpret the quotient in the context of your problem.

_____

 Turn and Talk Does it matter what visual model you use to find the quotient of a unit fraction divided by a whole number? Why might you choose one model over another? Explain.

Check Understanding [Math Board]

1 Write and solve a word problem for the equation $\frac{1}{5} \div 2 = c$. Represent the quotient using the rectangle.

_____

_____

_____

2 Complete the word problem that is represented by the equation $m = \frac{1}{6} \div 3$. Then draw a visual model to represent the quotient.

_____ friends share _____ of a bag of marbles

equally. Each friend gets _____ of the whole bag.

On Your Own

3 (MP) **Model with Mathematics** Write a word problem for the equation $\frac{1}{4} \div 4 = c$. Then write a related multiplication equation to solve.

_____

_____

_____

4 (MP) **Use Tools** Use the circle to write and solve a word problem involving a clock for $m = \frac{1}{2} \div 6$.

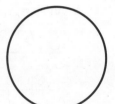

_____

_____

(MP) **Model with Mathematics** Complete the word problem to represent the equation. Then draw a visual model to represent and solve the problem.

5 $\frac{1}{5} \div 6 = c$

Julie cleans _____ carpets using _____ of a bottle of cleaner. She uses the same amount for each carpet. She

uses _____ of a bottle on one carpet.

6 (MP) **Attend to Precision** For the equation $\frac{1}{8} \div 2 = r$:

- Write a word problem.

_____

_____

- Draw a visual model to represent the quotient.

- Interpret the quotient in the context of your word problem.

_____

7 (MP) **Use Tools** Use the rectangle to represent $\frac{1}{8} \div 3 = p$. Then write and solve a word problem that can be modeled by the equation.

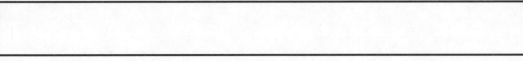

_____

_____

8 (MP) **Attend to Precision** For the equation $b = \frac{1}{10} \div 4$:

- Write a word problem.

  _____

  _____

- Draw a visual model to represent the quotient.

- How are the dividend and divisor represented by your visual model?

  _____

  _____

- Interpret the quotient in the context of your problem.

  _____

9 (MP) **Reason** For $\frac{1}{4} \div 6 = t$, Lena writes the word problem: "A string is 6 feet long. Jen wants to cut the string into $\frac{1}{4}$-foot pieces. How many pieces will Jen get?" Why does the word problem not make sense for this equation?

_____

_____

Name _____

Solve Division Problems Using Visual Models and Equations

(I Can) solve problems involving the division of fractions and whole numbers.

Step It Out

1 Rohan and Sim are building a terrarium. The first layer is made of sand. They can use a scoop to add sand to make the first layer. Rohan has a $\frac{1}{3}$-cup scoop and Sim has a $\frac{1}{4}$-cup scoop.

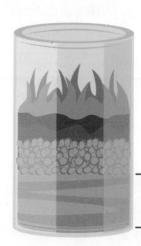

3 cups of sand

A. Write and solve an equation to model the number of scoops needed to fill the first layer if only Rohan's scoop is used. How many scoops are needed?

_____

B. Write and solve an equation to model the number of scoops needed to fill the first layer if only Sim's scoop is used. How many scoops are needed?

_____

C. If Rohan's scoop and Sim's scoop are used to add sand in whole-number cup amounts, what are possible numbers of scoops that each would add? _____

_____

D. Use equations, visual models, or words to justify your answers in Part C.

_____

_____

 Turn and Talk How would your answers change if Sim had a $\frac{1}{2}$-cup scoop?

Step It Out

2 The next layer in the terrarium is made using all of the pebbles in Rohan's bag. If he uses 5 scoops, about how many kilograms of pebbles does the scoop hold?

A. Write a division equation to model this situation.

_____

B. Use a visual model to solve the problem.

C. What does the quotient mean in the context of the story?

_____

 Turn and Talk How could you solve this problem using multiplication?

• •

Check Understanding [Math Board]

1 Rohan plants seeds in the terrarium. He wants the plants to grow to be 6 inches tall. If the plants grow $\frac{1}{3}$ inch per week, how many weeks will it take for the plants to grow to be 6 inches tall? Draw a visual model to represent the situation and solve the problem. Then write a division equation to model the problem.

On Your Own

2 (MP) **Model with Mathematics** A truck can carry $\frac{1}{2}$ ton of oil. The oil is transported equally in 5 drums. How much does one drum of oil weigh? Draw a visual fraction model to represent the situation and solve the problem. Then write a division equation to model the problem.

3 (MP) **Model with Mathematics** An ice cream shop has a container with 16 cups of chocolate ice cream. Each scoop of ice cream is $\frac{1}{2}$ cup. How many scoops of chocolate ice cream can the shop serve? Model this situation with a division equation and write a related multiplication equation to solve.

Divide. Write a related multiplication equation to solve.

4 $9 \div \frac{1}{8} = n$

5 $n = \frac{1}{5} \div 7$

6 $\frac{1}{8} \div 6 = n$

7 (MP) **Use Tools** Olivia has 9 yards of ribbon to make bows. Each bow uses $\frac{1}{3}$ yard of ribbon. How many bows can Olivia make?

- Draw a visual fraction model to represent the situation and solve the problem.

- How many bows can Olivia make? Write a division equation to model the problem.

On Your Own

8 (MP) **Use Tools** To make a homemade "lava lamp," you can mix vegetable oil, food coloring, and $\frac{1}{4}$ tablet of baking soda. How many lava lamps can you make if you have 5 tablets of baking soda?

- Draw a visual fraction model to represent the situation and solve the problem.

- How many lava lamps can you make? Write a division equation to model the problem.

  _____

9 (MP) **Model with Mathematics** Six friends are sharing a $\frac{1}{4}$-pound package of beads equally. What fraction of a pound of beads does each friend get?

- Write a division equation to model the situation.

  _____

- Write a related multiplication equation to solve.

  _____

- What fraction of a pound of beads does each friend get?

  _____

10 (MP) **Construct Arguments** How does the quotient of a unit fraction divided by a whole number compare to the quotient of a whole number divided by a unit fraction?

  _____

  _____

  _____

Review

Concepts and Skills

1 Write a word problem that can be modeled by the equation $2 \div \frac{1}{8} = m$. Then draw a visual fraction model to represent and solve the problem.

_____

_____

2 Usain has $\frac{1}{2}$ bag of cat food. He feeds an equal amount of the bag to his cat each day for 8 days. What fraction of the whole bag does he feed his cat each day? Write a division equation and a related multiplication equation to solve.

_____

3 (MP) **Use Tools** Sienna is making origami stars. Each star uses a strip of paper. She has 36 sheets of origami paper, and cuts out strips that are $\frac{1}{2}$ of each sheet. How many origami stars can Sienna make? Tell what strategy or tool you will use to answer the question, explain your choice, and then find the answer.

_____

_____

4 Which division equation correctly represents the number line?

(A) $\frac{1}{4} \div 3 = x$ (C) $3 \div \frac{1}{4} = x$

(B) $\frac{1}{3} \div 4 = x$ (D) $4 \div \frac{1}{3} = x$

5 Use the expression $\frac{1}{2} \div 12$ to complete the word problem. Then draw a visual fraction model to represent and solve the problem.

Trevor has _____ days to finish illustrating _____ of a book. If the time he spends illustrating is an equal amount each day, how much of the whole book will Trevor illustrate each day?

_____

Divide. Write a related multiplication equation to solve.

6 $11 \div \frac{1}{5} = n$ _____

7 $n = \frac{1}{3} \div 18$ _____

8 Fiona's mom makes $\frac{1}{4}$ gallon of raspberry lemonade for Fiona and her 3 friends for a picnic lunch. Select all the equations that represent the fraction of a gallon of raspberry lemonade that Fiona and her 3 friends will each get.

Ⓐ $\frac{1}{4} \times \frac{1}{4} = r$

Ⓑ $\frac{1}{4} \times \frac{1}{3} = r$

Ⓒ $3 \div \frac{1}{4} = r$

Ⓓ $4 \div \frac{1}{4} = r$

Ⓔ $\frac{1}{4} \div 4 = r$

Ⓕ $\frac{1}{4} \times 3 = r$

12 Customary Measurement

Who WON the high jump?

- Use the table to award the medals for the high jump competition.

HIGH JUMP COMPETITION			
Competitor	Height of Jump	Competitor	Height of Jump
Ariana	73 inches	Erika	49 inches
Bridget	1 yard	Frederica	5 feet
Christine	4 feet	Georgia	3 feet
Darlene	59 inches	Hong	2 yards

_____ _____ _____

 Turn and Talk

- Which do you think would be the best unit to use to compare the heights? Explain your answer.

- How did you solve the problem?

Are You Ready?

Complete these problems to review prior concepts and skills you will need for this module.

Measure Length to the Nearest Inch

Use an inch ruler. Measure the length to the nearest inch.

1 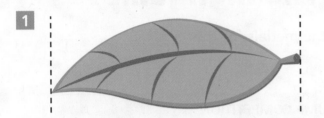 _____ in.

2 _____ in.

2-Digit by 1-Digit Multiplication

Find the product.

3 54
     × 3

4 12
     × 8

5 62
     × 3

6 49
     × 6

7 85
     × 5

8 12
     × 6

Choose Customary Units

Use benchmarks for length to choose the appropriate unit to measure each. Write *inch*, *foot*, *yard*, or *mile*.

9 distance between your home and the next city

10 width of your math book

_____   _____

Name

Convert Customary Measurements

(I Can) compare and convert customary units of measurement.

Spark Your Learning

Mount Rainier, in the state of Washington, is one of the snowiest places on Earth. During one winter snowstorm, a meteorologist predicted $15\frac{1}{2}$ feet of snow at Mount Rainier. Another meteorologist predicted 156 inches of snow. Which snow prediction is greater? By how much?

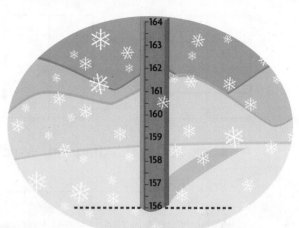

Show your thinking.

PAIRS

Turn and Talk Which conversion do you find easier—converting feet to inches or inches to feet? Explain.

Build Understanding

1 Aliyah converts 8 pints to gallons using a visual representation.

Measurement Conversion to a Larger Unit

8 pints ÷ 2 = 4 quarts ÷ 4 = 1 gallon

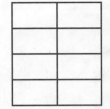 larger unit 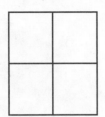 larger unit

pint   quart   gallon

A. Look at Aliyah's diagram. Which unit is the smallest? How do you know? _____

B. Which unit is the largest? How do you know?

_____

C. Are there more or fewer of the smaller unit? _____

D. Are there more or fewer of the larger unit? _____

E. What operation do you use to convert from a smaller unit to a larger unit? _____

F. Look at the **liquid volume** conversions in the table. How would you convert a number of fluid ounces to a number of cups? How do you know?

Customary Liquid Volume Conversions
1 cup (c) = 8 fluid ounces (fl oz)
1 pint (pt) = 2 cups
1 quart (qt) = 2 pints
1 gallon (gal) = 4 quarts

_____

_____

_____

G. How many cups are in 32 fluid ounces? _____

 Turn and Talk How would the steps change if the picture was reversed and you had to convert from gallons to pints?

© Houghton Mifflin Harcourt Publishing Company • Image Credit: ©Houghton Mifflin Harcourt

Step It Out

2 A cubic foot of light, fluffy snow weighs about 88 ounces. About how many pounds does a cubic foot of light, fluffy snow weigh?

88 ounces of snow

A. How many ounces are equal to 1 pound?

_____

B. Look at the **weight** conversions in the table. How do you convert a number of ounces to a number of pounds? How do you know?

Customary Weight Conversions
1 pound (lb) = 16 ounces (oz)
1 ton (T) = 2,000 pounds

_____

_____

_____

C. Write an expression to find the number of pounds of snow.

_____

D. How much does a cubic foot of light, fluffy snow weighing approximately 88 ounces weigh in pounds and ounces?

_____ lb _____ oz

E. What fraction of a pound is the number of ounces? How do you know?

_____

_____

F. How many pounds does the cubic foot of snow weigh?

_____

Turn and Talk How would you convert back to ounces if you were given the weight of the snow in pounds?

Step It Out

3 A frog jumps 48 inches. How many yards does the frog jump?

Sometimes you may need to use more than one conversion.

A. How can you use the **length** conversions in the table to convert from inches to yards?

_____

_____

Customary Length Conversions
1 foot (ft) = 12 inches (in.)
1 yard (yd) = 3 feet
1 mile (mi) = 5,280 feet
1 mile = 1,760 yards

B. How do you convert a number of inches to a

number of feet? _____

C. How many feet are in 48 inches? _____

D. How do you convert a number of feet to a

number of yards? _____

E. Write the number of yards as a mixed number. How many yards does the frog jump?

_____

 Turn and Talk For each of the three tasks, you converted a smaller unit of measurement to a larger unit. What conclusion can you draw about this kind of conversion?

Check Understanding

1 There are about 18 cups of water in a cubic foot of snow. About how many pints of water are in a cubic foot of snow?

_____

Convert.

2 90 in. = _____ ft

3 100 oz = _____ lb _____ oz

On Your Own

4 STEM Gold is a rare element. Its properties make it a valuable natural resource. The soft metal is used to make items such as coins and jewelry. Gold conducts electricity and often is used in the manufacturing of electronics. The largest gold nugget found with a metal detector weighs 960 ounces. If the value of gold is about $20,000 for one pound, what is the value of the nugget?

_____

5 (MP) Construct Arguments Will a 24-gallon tank hold 200 pints of water? Explain.

_____

_____

Convert.

6 126 in. = _____ ft _____ in.

7 20 fl oz = _____ c _____ fl oz

8 160 fl oz = _____ qt

9 72 qt = _____ gal

10 104 oz = _____ lb

11 4,200 lb = _____ T

12 23 ft = _____ yd _____ ft

13 132 in. = _____ yd

14 An elephant at the zoo weighs $4\frac{1}{2}$ tons. How many pounds does the elephant weigh? _____

15 A quarterback completed passes to his receivers and gained a total of 2,640 yards. How many miles was this? _____

16 A typical adult drinks 20 cups of warm beverages each week. How many gallons of warm beverages does a typical adult drink each week? _____

On Your Own

17 The world record for the longest mustache is 14 feet. How many yards and inches is this?

_____

18 **Reason** If you multiply by a factor of 16 to convert a larger unit of measurement to a smaller unit, by what factor would you multiply to convert the smaller unit of measurement to the larger unit? Explain your reasoning.

_____

_____

19 **Open Ended** Write a word problem that involves converting between pints and fluid ounces, and give the answer.

_____

_____

I'm in a Learning Mindset!

What strategies did I use to organize the information for comparing and converting customary units of measurement?

_____

© Houghton Mifflin Harcourt Publishing Company • Image Credit: ©Sam Panthaky/AFP/Getty Images

Name _____

Solve Multistep Customary Measurement Problems

(I Can) solve multistep problems that include customary measurement conversions.

Step It Out

1. Ezra is building the bookcase shown. All the pieces of wood are the same width. He needs two pieces of wood for the sides. He needs three pieces of wood for the shelves and the top.

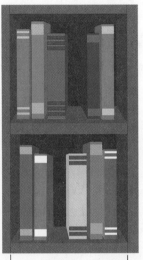

$3\frac{1}{2}$ ft

24 in.

What is the total length, in yards, of the wood Ezra needs to build the bookcase?

A. Write an equation to find how many feet of

wood Ezra needs for both sides. _____

B. Write an equation to find how many yards of

wood Ezra needs for both sides. _____

C. Write an equation to find how many inches of wood Ezra needs for the shelves and the top.

_____

D. Write two equations to find how many yards of wood Ezra needs for the shelves and top. First convert inches to feet.

_____

E. Write an equation to find how many yards of wood Ezra needs to build the bookcase.

_____

> **Turn and Talk** Is there another set of solution steps that would result in the correct answer? Explain.

Step it Out

2 Leanne needs 100 cups of lemonade for guests at a picnic. Each package of lemonade mix makes 1 gallon and costs $3.00. How much will it cost Leanne to make enough lemonade?

A. First find the number of gallons of lemonade Leanne needs. Convert the number of cups needed to a number of pints, then to a number of quarts, and then to a number of gallons.

- Write an equation to find how many pints of lemonade Leanne needs to make.

  _____

- Write an equation to find how many quarts of lemonade Leanne needs to make.

  _____

- Write an equation to find how many gallons of lemonade Leanne needs to make.

  _____

B. How many packages of lemonade does Leanne need to buy? Explain.

  _____

  _____

C. How much will it cost Leanne to make enough lemonade? How do you know?

  _____

  _____

 Turn and Talk How can you convert from cups to gallons with one calculation?

Check Understanding

1 Ezra arranges his neighbor's books on the bookshelf he built. Each hardcover book weighs 1 pound 2 ounces. Each paperback weighs 15 ounces. A shelf can hold up to 20 pounds. Can a shelf hold 9 hardcover books and 12 paperback books? Explain.

_____

_____

_____

2 Gina is making a banner for the school dance that is 84 inches long. The material to make the banner costs $6 for each yard. How much does Gina have to pay to buy the exact amount of material she needs?

_____

_____

On Your Own

3 (MP) **Reason** One gallon of apple juice costs $4. At this price, will nine 1-pint bottles or five 1-quart bottles of apple juice cost more? How much more? Explain.

_____

_____

_____

_____

4 (MP) **Reason** Michelle walks from her home to her work and back 4 days each week. Martin takes a 3-mile walk 3 days each week. Who walks farther in a week? By how many yards?

On Your Own

5 A basking shark measures $25\frac{1}{4}$ feet long. A giant squid measures $33\frac{1}{3}$ feet long. How many inches longer is the basking shark than the giant squid?

 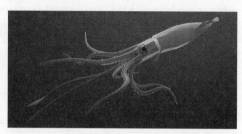

---

6 **(MP) Reason** A package of sliced cheese weighs $2\frac{1}{4}$ pounds and costs $18. If 3 slices weigh a total of 2 ounces, how much do the

3 slices cost? _____

7 A mother opossum weighs $9\frac{1}{2}$ pounds. She carries in her pouch 8 babies that weigh 14 ounces apiece. How many pounds do the mother opossum and her 8 babies weigh?

---

8 A beaded necklace is $2\frac{1}{2}$ feet long. Each bead is $\frac{1}{4}$ inch wide, and each pair of beads is separated by $1\frac{1}{4}$ inches of chain. How many beads are on the necklace?

---

9 The frame of a bicycle weighs 16 pounds. Each tire weighs 9 ounces. The seat weighs 12 ounces. The handlebars weigh 24 ounces. How many pounds does the bicycle weigh?

---

10 **Open Ended** A car's gas tank holds $13\frac{1}{2}$ gallons of gas. Explain how you could convert this measurement to pints.

Name _____

Represent and Interpret Measurement Data in Line Plots

(I Can) make a line plot to display data in fractional measurements and use the line plot to solve problems.

Step It Out

1 Students measured different amounts of water into their beakers for an experiment. If the total amount of water is redistributed equally, how much water will be in each beaker?

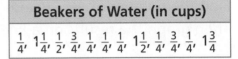

Beakers of Water (in cups)
$\frac{1}{4}$, $1\frac{1}{4}$, $\frac{1}{2}$, $\frac{3}{4}$, $\frac{1}{4}$, $\frac{1}{4}$, $\frac{1}{4}$, $1\frac{1}{2}$, $\frac{1}{4}$, $\frac{3}{4}$, $\frac{1}{4}$, $1\frac{3}{4}$

A. Complete the **line plot** by recording the data for the beakers. The first two amounts have been recorded.

B. How many cups of water are in the beakers that contain $\frac{1}{4}$ cup of water?

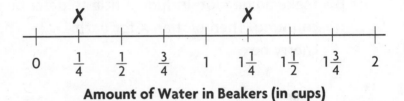

Amount of Water in Beakers (in cups)

_____

C. What is the total number of cups of water? _____

D. How many beakers are there? _____

E. Redistribute the water equally among all the beakers. How many cups of water will be in each beaker?

_____

Turn and Talk How would the redistribution change if there were four more beakers with $1\frac{1}{2}$ cups of water in each beaker?

Step it Out

2 ▶ Lamar divides three 2-pound boxes of cherries into smaller boxes. The first box is divided into boxes weighing $\frac{1}{8}$ pound each, the second box is divided into boxes weighing $\frac{1}{4}$ pound each, and the third box is divided into boxes weighing $\frac{1}{2}$ pound each.

2 lb

Find the number of $\frac{1}{8}$-, $\frac{1}{4}$-, and $\frac{1}{2}$-pound cherry boxes. Then graph the results on a line plot.

A. Use division to find the number of $\frac{1}{8}$-pound, $\frac{1}{4}$-pound, and $\frac{1}{2}$-pound boxes that were made from the three original 2-pound boxes of cherries.

$$2 \div \frac{1}{8} \qquad\qquad 2 \div \frac{1}{4} \qquad\qquad 2 \div \frac{1}{2}$$

$2 \times \underline{\hspace{1cm}} = \underline{\hspace{1cm}}$ $2 \times \underline{\hspace{1cm}} = \underline{\hspace{1cm}}$ $2 \times \underline{\hspace{1cm}} = \underline{\hspace{1cm}}$

B. Make a line plot. Include a title to describe what you are counting. Then plot an ✗ for each $\frac{1}{8}$-, $\frac{1}{4}$-, and $\frac{1}{2}$-pound cherry box.

C. How many more $\frac{1}{8}$-pound cherry boxes are there than $\frac{1}{2}$-pound cherry boxes? _____

 Turn and Talk Explain why there are more $\frac{1}{8}$-pound cherry boxes than $\frac{1}{2}$-pound cherry boxes.

Check Understanding

1 Charles poured different amounts of milk into some bowls. Show the amounts on the line plot.

Bowls of Milk (in pints)

$\frac{1}{8}, \frac{1}{4}, \frac{1}{2}, \frac{1}{4}, \frac{1}{8}, \frac{1}{4}, \frac{1}{4}, \frac{1}{4}$

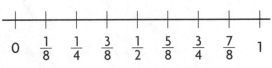

Amount of Milk in Bowls (in pints)

2 What is the total amount of milk that Charles poured?

3 If Charles redistributed the milk equally among the bowls, how much milk would he pour into each bowl?

_____   _____

On Your Own

4 A scientist records the weights of her mineral specimens.

Make a line plot to display the data.

Mineral Specimen Weights (in ounces)

$\frac{1}{2}, \frac{1}{2}, 1, \frac{1}{2}, \frac{1}{4}, 1\frac{1}{2}, 1\frac{1}{2}, 1, 1\frac{1}{4}$

Use your line plot for 5–7.

5 What is the total weight of the mineral specimens? _____

6 What is the combined weight of the $\frac{1}{2}$-ounce and

$1\frac{1}{2}$-ounce specimens? _____

7 How much more do the $1\frac{1}{2}$-ounce specimens weigh than the

$\frac{1}{2}$-ounce specimens? _____

On Your Own

Use the line plot for 8–11.

Anita grows aquatic plants in jars. The jars hold different amounts of water. Anita records the amounts of water the jars hold in a line plot.

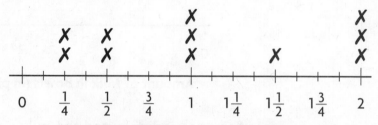

Amount of Water in Jars (in gallons)

8 What is the total liquid volume of the water in the jars?

_____

9 How many more jars have 2 gallons of water than have

$1\frac{1}{2}$ gallons? _____

10 How much water is in all the $\frac{1}{4}$-gallon jars? _____

11 If Anita transfers the water in the 1-gallon jars to $\frac{3}{4}$-gallon jars,

how many $\frac{3}{4}$-gallon jars does she need? _____

12 (MP) **Reason** Michaela records the amount of water in 15 beakers. She determines that she must redistribute 3 fluid ounces to each beaker for all of them to have an equal amount. Then she realizes that the total amount of water is actually 5 fluid ounces more than she first calculated. What happens to the amount she equally redistributes? Explain.

_____

_____

_____

_____

Name _____

Convert Time and Find Elapsed Time

(I Can) solve elapsed time problems by converting units of time.

Step It Out

1 Claudio wants to ride the exercise bike at least 5 hours each week. He recorded the amount of time he rode the exercise bike each day last week. Did Claudio reach his goal last week?

Time Riding Exercise Bike							
Day	Sunday	Monday	Tuesday	Wednesday	Thursday	Friday	Saturday
Number of Minutes	50	35	30	45	40	30	50

A. Find the total number of minutes Claudio rode the bike. _____

B. How can you convert the number of minutes to a number of hours?

_____

C. How many hours did Claudio ride the exercise bike last week? Write the answer as a mixed number.

_____

D. Did Claudio reach his goal? Explain.

_____

Time Conversions
1 minute (min) = 60 seconds (sec)
1 hour (hr) = 60 minutes
1 day (d) = 24 hours
1 week (wk) = 7 days
1 year (yr) = about 52 weeks
1 year = 365 days

 Turn and Talk Claudio rode the exercise bike for 7,920 minutes in the past year. Explain how to convert this number of minutes to an equivalent number of days.

2 Abram arrives at the swim meet at 9:30 a.m. and stays for 225 minutes. At what time does he leave?

A. Find the number of hours Abram is at the swim meet. Convert 225 minutes to a number of hours. For how many hours is Abram at the meet? _____

B. Use a number line with increments of 15 minutes to represent the **elapsed time**. Count the number of whole hours and then the number of quarter-hours.

$\frac{1}{4}$ hour = 15 minutes

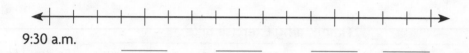

9:30 a.m.

_____   _____   _____   _____

C. At what time does Abram leave? _____

 Turn and Talk Terrance leaves the swim meet at the same time as Abram. If he was at the swim meet for $2\frac{1}{2}$ hours, how can you determine at what time he arrived?

• •

Check Understanding Math Board

1 Two weeks ago, Claudio rode the exercise bike each day for these numbers of minutes: 45, 35, 50, 20, 40, 40, and 30. Did he reach his goal of riding at least 5 hours each week? Explain.

_____

2 Marcus gets to the library at 11:00 a.m. He stays for 150 minutes.

At what time does he leave the library? _____

Convert.

3 495 min = _____ hr

4 35 d = _____ wk

5 300 sec = _____ min

6 $2\frac{1}{2}$ yr = about _____ wk

On Your Own

7 (MP) **Use Tools** Ms. Luz looks at the clock at the airport. Her flight is scheduled to leave at 2:15 p.m. How long does Ms. Luz have to wait?

- What time is it now? _____

- Use the number line to show how long Ms. Luz has to wait.

- How long does Ms. Luz wait in hours and minutes?

  _____ hr _____ min

- How many hours does Ms. Luz have to wait?

  _____

8 Dmitri practiced playing the saxophone for 225 minutes last week. Lauren practiced for $3\frac{3}{4}$ hours. Who practiced more? Explain how you know.

_____

_____

_____

Convert.

9 330 sec = _____ min _____ sec

10 130 hr = _____ d _____ hr

11 182 wk = about _____ yr

12 560 min = _____ hr

13 490 sec = _____ min

14 $5\frac{1}{3}$ d = _____ hr

15 $3\frac{1}{2}$ min = _____ sec

16 4 yr = _____ d

On Your Own

Find the start, elapsed, or end time.

17 Start time: 11:15 a.m.

Elapsed time: $5\frac{1}{2}$ hr

End time: _____

18 Start time: 9:30 a.m.

Elapsed time: 380 min

End time: _____

19 Start time: 10:45 a.m.

Elapsed time: _____ hr _____ min

End time: 6:15 p.m.

20 Start time: _____

Elapsed time: $8\frac{1}{6}$ hr

End time: 3:30 p.m.

Compare. Write <, >, or =.

21 $1\frac{1}{2}$ yr ◯ 80 wk

22 500 min ◯ $8\frac{1}{4}$ hr

23 $2\frac{1}{5}$ hr ◯ 7,920 sec

24 1 wk ◯ 180 hr

25 Tasha looks at her watch at the start and at the end of the concert. How long was the concert? Give the elapsed time in hours and in minutes.

_____

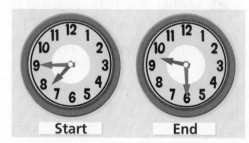

Start   End

26 (MP) **Reason** Explain how you can find the number of hours in one week.

_____

_____

27 **Open Ended** Write an elapsed-time problem that has an answer of $5\frac{3}{4}$ hours.

_____

_____

_____

Review

Concepts and Skills

1 A carpenter builds a ladder for a tree house. Each of the two sides of the ladder is $7\frac{1}{2}$ feet long. Each of the five rungs is 18 inches long. How many yards of wood does the carpenter need to build the ladder?

(A) $7\frac{1}{2}$ yd

(B) $22\frac{1}{2}$ yd

(C) $25\frac{1}{2}$ yd

(D) 270 yd

2 The anaconda is the world's largest snake. A typical adult anaconda is 17 feet long. What is the length of a typical

adult anaconda in yards and feet? _____ yards _____ feet

3 Susie has a 22-quart bucket full of water. A hole at the bottom allows 1 cup of water to leak out each minute. How many minutes will it take for the bucket to have $1\frac{1}{2}$ gallons of water

left in it? _____

4 (MP) **Use Tools** The current time is shown on the clock. Use the times to complete the table. Tell what strategy or tool you will use to solve the problem, explain your choice, and then find the answers.

| 12:35 | 3:30 | 12:05 | 4:05 |

$2\frac{1}{4}$ hours later	
$2\frac{5}{6}$ hours from now	
$\frac{2}{3}$ hour earlier	
$1\frac{1}{6}$ hours before	

Use the line plot for 5–6.

Stan cuts a piece of rope into the lengths shown on the line plot.

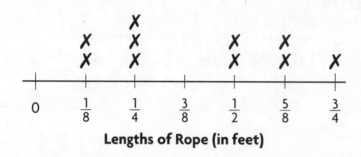

Lengths of Rope (in feet)

5 What was the length of the rope before Stan cut it?

_____

6 What is the combined length of the $\frac{1}{8}$-foot and $\frac{1}{4}$-foot pieces?

_____

Convert.

7 36 fl oz = _____ c

8 55 fl oz = _____ c _____ fl oz

9 195 min = _____ hours

10 73 hr = _____ d _____ hr

11 Kevin buys a bag of mixed nuts with $1\frac{1}{2}$ pounds of peanuts, 11 ounces of cashews, $\frac{1}{4}$ pound of Brazil nuts, and 1 pound 5 ounces of walnuts. Select all the amounts that show the weight of the nuts in the bag.

Ⓐ $2\frac{3}{4}$ pounds

Ⓑ 3 pounds 12 ounces

Ⓒ $3\frac{3}{4}$ pounds

Ⓓ $3\frac{3}{4}$ ounces

Ⓔ 60 ounces

Add and Subtract Decimals

Fundraising Director

Fundraising directors are responsible for raising money for charities and non-profit organizations to help people in need, work to rescue animals, advocate for environmental issues, and so on. They think of ways to connect with and motivate potential donors. They may use advertisements, email, and letters to ask for donations.

Fundraising directors must also make speeches and attend events. They must also stay up-to-date on current events in order to speak with possible donors.

STEM Task:

Play with a partner. Use digit cards (0–9) and the chart on the next page. Choose 12 cards, one at a time, and write the digit in one of the spaces for expenses or donations. Place the digit where it helps the most! Once you place a digit, you may not move it. When all twelve digits are placed, add the donations and subtract the expenses. The player who has the greater total wins. Play again using some of the strategies you learned when playing the first time.

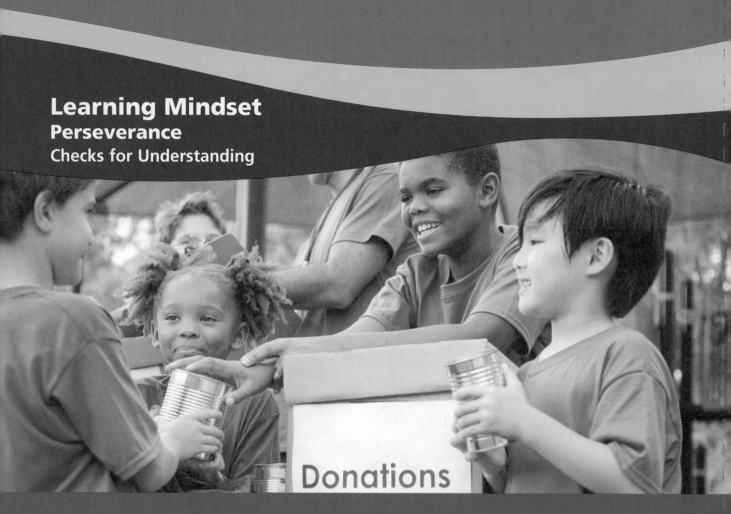

Learning Mindset
Perseverance
Checks for Understanding

Donations

It can take time to learn successful strategies for any task, even when the task is a game. When you play any game that requires strategy, reflect on the success of your strategies as you play. Ask yourself: "Do I know why that worked or didn't work?" Then modify your strategies to improve the result as you play. You can also learn a lot from other players by watching the strategies they use.

Reflect

Q Did you understand the purpose of and directions for the STEM Task? How do you know you understood?

Q Describe the strategies you used to get the greater total.

Player 1		Player 2	
Donation	$ _____ , _____ _____ _____	Donation	$ _____ , _____ _____ _____
Donation	$ _____ , _____ _____ _____	Donation	$ _____ , _____ _____ _____
Expenses	$ _____ , _____ _____ _____	Expenses	$ _____ , _____ _____ _____
Total	$ _____ , _____ _____ _____	Total	$ _____ , _____ _____ _____

Decimal Place Value

What is the combination?

- Oh no! You forgot the combination to the bicycle lock. Use the clues to figure out the combination.

Clue 1 The combination is a 4-digit number with all different digits.

Clue 2 The value of the digit in the thousands place is 300 times as much as the value of the digit in the tens place.

Clue 3 The value of the digit in the hundreds place is 20 times as much as the value of the digit in the ones place.

Clue 4 The value of the digit in the tens place is 70 less than the value of the digit in the hundreds place.

Clue 5 The digit with the least place value is 5.

The combination is _____.

 Turn and Talk

- How did you solve the problem?

- What are some other clues that use place value that you could write for the same combination?

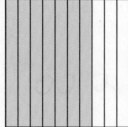

Are You Ready?

Complete these problems to review prior concepts and skills you will need for this module.

Represent Tenths and Hundredths

Write the amount shown as a fraction and as a decimal.

1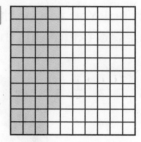

Fraction: _____

Decimal: _____

2

Fraction: _____

Decimal: _____

Compare Decimals

Write <, >, or = to compare the decimals.

3 0.6 ◯ 0.63   4 1.40 ◯ 1.42   5 2.70 ◯ 2.7

6 0.58 ◯ 0.61   7 1.22 ◯ 1.32   8 3.6 ◯ 3.5

Equivalent Decimals

Write the equivalent decimal in hundredths.

9 3.4   10 2.8   11 10.1

_____   _____   _____

Write the equivalent decimal in tenths.

12 6.50   13 5.90   14 0.40

_____   _____   _____

Name _____

Understand Thousandths

(**I Can**) describe the relationship between two decimal place-value positions to the thousandths place.

Spark Your Learning

Kiana is looking at seawater under a microscope to search for microscopic organisms. A droplet of seawater has a mass of about 51.3 milligrams.

What would be the mass of 10 droplets of seawater? Show your reasoning.

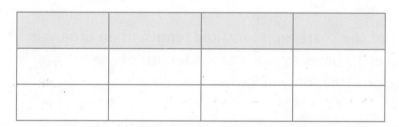

 Turn and Talk Kiana puts 10 droplets of freshwater in a test tube. The droplets have a mass of about 499.0 milligrams. What would you expect the mass of one droplet of freshwater to be? How do you know?

Build Understanding

1 DeShawn measures the length of a phytoplankton under a microscope as 0.1 mm. Use the place-value chart to answer the questions.

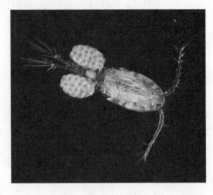

Ones	· Tenths	Hundredths	Thousandths
flat	rod	cube	

A. Which part of the chart represents the length of the phytoplankton? How do you know?

The Rod that represents (0.1)

B. Which part of the chart represents the length of an organism that measures 10 times as much as the length of the phytoplankton? How do you know?

The flat or the ones place.

C. Which part of the chart represents the length of an organism that measures $\frac{1}{10}$ of the length of the phytoplankton? How do you know?

The cube or the hundreths place.

D. How could you represent thousandths in the chart?

Cut the cube into ten parts.

Connect to Vocabulary

A **thousandth** is one of one thousand equal parts.
Example:
0.008 = eight thousandths

2 The length of a sea creature, the anemone, measures 0.04 inch early in its development. It is about 10 times as thick as a sheet of paper and $\frac{1}{10}$ of the width of a vitamin.

A. Use the place-value chart to represent each measure.

	Ones	Tenths	Hundredths	Thousandths
anemone				
paper				
vitamin				

B. What patterns in the chart can you describe?

_____

_____

_____

C. What are the measures of the three items?

_____

 Turn and Talk How do the place-value positions with decimals compare to the place-value positions with whole numbers?

• •

Check Understanding

1 Ten pennies weigh about 0.9 ounce. About how much does

one penny weigh? _____

2 One dime weighs about 0.005 pound. About how much do

10 dimes weigh? _____

On Your Own

[handwritten at top: mutiply something by ten decimil moves one place to the right]

[handwritten: multiply decimel by 1/10 move decimil to the left]

3 (MP) **Use Tools** Complete the table to write numbers that are 10 times as much as, and $\frac{1}{10}$ of, 0.5.

[handwritten left: 0.5 →]

10 times as much as	Decimal	$\frac{1}{10}$ of
5.	0.5	.05

[handwritten right: 0.5]

Write the number that is 10 times as much as the number.

4 0.002

00.2

5 8,739

87.39

6 35.4

354.

Write the number that is $\frac{1}{10}$ of the number.

7 0.25

.025

8 5,019.72

5,01.972

9 3.6

.36

10 (MP) **Reason** Five hundredths multiplied by what number is five thousandths? Explain.

_____

11 (MP) **Use Structure** In the number 9.689, how does the value of the digit 9 to the left of the decimal point compare to the value of the digit 9 to the right of the decimal point?

_____

_____

 I'm in a Learning Mindset!

What do I do when I'm learning something new? What helps me remember what to do?

_____

_____

© Houghton Mifflin Harcourt Publishing Company

Name

Read and Write Decimals to Thousandths

(I Can) read, write, and represent decimals to thousandths.

Spark Your Learning

A digital caliper can measure the lengths of objects to the nearest thousandth inch.

How would you read the measurement shown? Describe the place value of each digit.

Hundreds	Tens	Ones

Turn and Talk How do you represent the decimal point when you say a decimal? Describe the numbers that are to the left and right of the decimal point.

Build Understanding

1 The Great Pyramid of Giza in Egypt originally stood 146.609 meters tall.

Write the height of the pyramid in the place-value chart. Then represent the height using words.

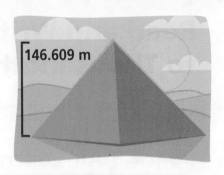

146.609 m

Hundreds	Tens	Ones •	Tenths	Hundredths	Thousandths

Hundreds	Tens	C

A. Do the two digits that are the same in 146.609 have the same place value? Explain.

_____

_____

B. Since the digit in the hundredths place is 0, can you write the decimal as 146.69? Explain.

_____

_____

C. To write 146.609 in expanded form, find the unknown numbers. Write the expanded form of 146.609.

$1 \times \blacksquare + 4 \times \blacksquare + 6 \times \blacksquare + 6 \times \blacksquare + 0 \times \blacksquare + 9 \times \blacksquare$

_____

 Turn and Talk How can you use the place value of the last digit in a decimal to help you read that decimal?

2 In building pyramids, Egyptians left a gap between the stones as shown. Would a grain of soil that measures five thousandths millimeter fit inside the gap?

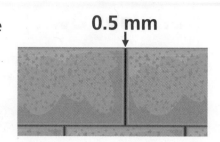

0.5 mm

A. Represent each measure in the chart.

Ones	•	Tenths	Hundredths	Thousandths
	•			
	•			

B. Complete the expanded form of each measure.

gap: _____ × _____

grain of soil: _____ × _____

C. How does the value of the digit 5 in each measure compare?

_____

D. Can a grain of soil fit in the gap? How do you know?

_____

_____

_____

 Turn and Talk How can you use place value to compare the last digit of two different decimal numbers?

Check Understanding [Math Board]

1 A digital caliper shows a measurement of 13.028 inches. Write the word form and expanded form of the number.

word form: _____

expanded form: _____

On Your Own

2 (MP) **Reason** What decimal has $\frac{1}{10}$ of the value of 0.8 and 10 times as much as the value of 0.008? Explain.

_____

_____

_____

3 (MP) **Use Structure** Complete the chart for the number 352.078.

Hundreds	Tens	Ones	•	Tenths	Hundredths	Thousandths
3	5	2	•	0	7	8

Hundreds	Tens	Ones	Tenths	Hundredths	Thousandths
3 × 100	5 × 10	2 × 1	0 × $\frac{1}{10}$		
300					

4 How would you read the decimal shown by the digital caliper?

_____

Write the number in standard form.

5 twenty-five thousand, forty-six and nine thousandths

_____

6 9 × 100 + 0 × 10 + 2 × 1 + 0 × 0.1 + 5 × 0.01 + 6 × 0.001

_____

_____

⊹ I'm in a Learning Mindset!

How effective was a place-value chart in helping me read, write, and represent decimals?

_____

Round Decimals

(**I Can**) use an understanding of place value to round decimals to a given place.

Spark Your Learning

In car racing, times are measured to the nearest thousandth second. The time it takes ten cars to make one lap around a short track is shown.

Short Track Lap Times (in seconds)			
Car 1	15.2	**Car 6**	14.45
Car 2	14.834	**Car 7**	15.503
Car 3	16.43	**Car 8**	14.498
Car 4	15.099	**Car 9**	16.04
Car 5	15.873	**Car 10**	14.53

Sort the cars into the boxes using the time for each car to the nearest second.

14 seconds

15 seconds

16 seconds

SMALL GROUPS

Hundreds	Tens	Ones

Turn and Talk How would a time of 15.045 seconds appear on a stopwatch that rounds to the nearest hundredth second? Explain.

Build Understanding

Lap Time: 28.266 seconds
134 MPH

1 In a long track car race, a driver's lap time was 28.266 seconds.

Label the tick marks. Show where the driver's time can be represented on the number line.

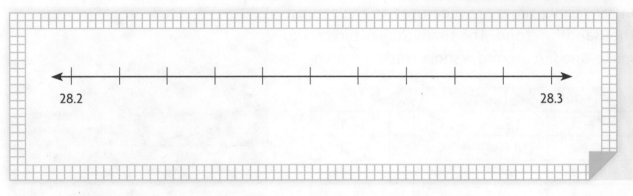

28.2   28.3

A. How could you divide the space between each pair of tick marks to show thousandths?

_____

_____

B. How can you determine to which hundredth second the driver's time is closer? Round 28.266 seconds to the nearest hundredth second.

_____

_____

C. How can you determine to which tenth second the driver's time is closer? Round 28.266 seconds to the nearest tenth second.

_____

_____

 Turn and Talk What are some possible driver's times that are closer to 28.26 than to 28.27?

© Houghton Mifflin Harcourt Publishing Company

Step It Out

2 Speeds also are measured to the nearest thousandth. The fastest speed in a race was 96.479 miles per hour (mph). Write the speed in the place-value chart.

Tens	Ones	Tenths	Hundredths	Thousandths

A. To round this speed to the nearest hundredth, circle the digit in the hundredths place in the chart.

B. Underline the digit to the right of the place to which you are rounding. How does this digit compare to 5?

_____

C. If the digit to the right is less than 5, the digit in the place to which you are rounding stays the same. If the digit to the right is 5 or greater, the digit in the rounding place increases by 1. Round the speed to the nearest hundredth.

_____

D. Round the speed to the nearest tenth and to the nearest whole number.

_____

 Turn and Talk How would your rounded numbers change if the speed was 96.515 mph?

Check Understanding

1 A professional race car driver's speed in a race was 212.809 mph. What is this speed rounded to the nearest hundredth, nearest tenth, and nearest whole number?

_____

       329

On Your Own

2 (MP) **Reason** The decimal 671.54■ rounds to 671.54. What are the possible values for ■?

_____

3 (MP) **Reason** What range of numbers, to thousandths, round to 146?

_____

Round 5.935 to the place named.

4 tenths   **5** hundredths   **6** ones

_____   _____   _____

Name the place value to which the number was rounded.

7 0.783 to 0.78   **8** 4.559 to 4.6   **9** 3.249 to 3.25

_____   _____   _____

10 (MP) **Attend to Precision** The gas tank of a race car holds up to 68.137 liters of gas. What is 68.137 liters rounded to the nearest hundredth, nearest tenth, and nearest whole liter?

_____

11 (MP) **Use Structure** A professional race car driver's speed was 342.483 kilometers each hour. When rounding this speed, in which place value would the digit in the rounding place increase by 1? Explain.

_____

_____

🎲 I'm in a Learning Mindset!

Did I try a new strategy to round numbers? What was it?

_____

© Houghton Mifflin Harcourt Publishing Company

Name _____

Compare and Order Decimals

(I Can) use place value to compare and order decimals
to thousandths.

Step It Out

1 The field goal percentage
(FG%) in basketball is found by
dividing the number of baskets
made (FG) by the number of
baskets attempted (FGA).

Hector compares the field goal
percentages for Thomas and Lucas.

Basketball Statistics					
Player	FG	FGA	FG%	FT	FTA
Thomas	32	67	0.478	15	21
Young	46	96	0.479	18	22
Lucas	35	74	0.473	24	28
Stanie	56	101	0.554	11	15

A. Compare each place value, working from left to
right, until you find a digit that is different. In
which place value are the digits different?

_____

B. Compare the digits in the place value that you
found in Part A. Use the less than symbol.

_____

C. Compare the digits using the greater than symbol.

_____

D. Compare the field goal percentages for Thomas
and Lucas in two different ways. Use the less than
symbol, and then use the greater than symbol.

_____

E. Which player has the higher field goal percentage?

_____

> **Connect to Vocabulary**
>
> The **less than (<)**
> symbol is the symbol
> used to compare
> two numbers or two
> quantities, with the
> lesser number or lesser
> quantity given first. The
> **greater than (>)** symbol
> is the symbol used to
> compare two numbers
> or two quantities when
> the greater number
> or greater quantity is
> given first.

 Turn and Talk Why is it important for the decimal points in
the table to be lined up?

© Houghton Mifflin Harcourt Publishing Company

Step It Out

2 ▶ The table shows the field goal percentages of three players.

Basketball Statistics	
Player	**Field Goal Percentage**
Ortega	0.447
Robinson	0.452
Alabi	0.449

A. What is the greatest place-value position in which you find a digit that is different?

_____

B. Use your answer from Part A. Which player has the greatest digit in this place-value position?

_____

C. Move to the next lesser place-value position and compare the digits of the other two players. Which player has the greater digit in this place-value position?

_____

D. Order the players, by name, by their field goal percentages from greatest to least.

_____

 Turn and Talk What would happen if you compare decimals working from right to left instead of left to right?

Check Understanding

1 Order from greatest to least.

475.314; 475.321; 475.412; 475.296

_____

Compare. Write <, >, or =.

2 76.924 ◯ 76.931

3 5,486.329 ◯ 5,486.326

On Your Own

4 (MP) **Attend to Precision** The table shows the free throw percentages of four players. Order the players, by name, by their free throw percentages from least to greatest.

Free Throw Percentage	
Player	**Free Throw Percentage**
Randall	0.796
Sampson	0.697
Carter	0.794
Lee	0.803

_____

5 (MP) **Reason** What are the possible digits that make the statement true?

98.346 > 98.■46

_____

6 The decimal 237.057 is greater than another decimal by one hundredth. What is the other decimal?

_____

Compare. Write <, >, or =.

7 8.391 ◯ 8.371

8 29.808 ◯ 29.088

9 6.091 ◯ 6.91

10 3.90 ◯ 3.9

11 1.532 ◯ 2.42

12 23.742 ◯ 13.742

13 (MP) **Reason** Given two numbers, if all digits to the right of the decimal point are the same, is it true that the two numbers are equal? Explain.

_____

_____

14 In baseball, the batting average is found by dividing the number of base hits by the number of times at bat. The table shows the batting averages for four baseball players. Order the players, by name, from greatest batting average to least batting average.

Batting Average	
Player	**Batting Average**
Jones	0.286
Gomez	0.288
Brotherton	0.278
Robledo	0.304

_____

_____

Compare. Write <, >, or =.

15 8,156.327 $\bigcirc$ 8,156.372

16 29.48 $\bigcirc$ 29.480

17 971.283 $\bigcirc$ 971.328

18 233.518 $\bigcirc$ 233.158

Order from least to greatest.

19 5.34; 5.314; 5.431; 5.134

20 7.389; 7.398; 7.399; 7.388

_____

_____

21 **STEM** The four planets in our solar system that are closest to the sun are called the inner planets. Mars is the farthest inner planet from the sun, and Mercury is the closest to the sun. Venus is closer to the sun than Earth. The approximate planet distances from the sun in billion kilometers are 0.15, 0.228, 0.058, and 0.108. Write the planets and their distance from the sun in order from closest to farthest.

_____

_____

22 **Open Ended** Think of a real-world situation involving decimals to the thousandths place. Write and solve a problem to order four decimals in the situation.

_____

_____

Module 13 Review

Vocabulary

Write the correct vocabulary word on the line.

1 To _____ means to replace a number with one that is simpler and is approximately the same size as the original number.

2 A _____ is one of one thousand equal parts.

3 The _____ symbol is the symbol used to compare two numbers or quantities, with the lesser number or lesser quantity given first.

Concepts and Skills

4 Find $\frac{1}{10}$ of 427.9.

(A) 4,279.0   (B) 42.79   (C) 4.279   (D) 0.427

5 Select all the numbers that are 10 times as much as 72.67 or $\frac{1}{10}$ of 72.67.

(A) 7.267

(B) 72.670

(C) 7,267.0

(D) 720.67

(E) 726.7

6 (MP) **Use Tools** In which number does the digit 5 have a value that is 10 times as much as the value of the digit 5 in 2.567? Tell what strategy or tool you will use to answer the question, explain your choice, and then find the answer.

(A) 0.539   (C) 2.951

(B) 2.185   (D) 5.246

7 What is 36,927.65 written in word form?

_____

8 What is 2,478.08 written in word form?

_____

9 What is 25.836 written in expanded form?

_____

10 What is 1,852.4 written in expanded form?

_____

11 The decimal 74.3■7 rounds to 74.4. What are the possible values of ■?

_____

12 Which is 37.847 rounded to the nearest hundredth?

Ⓐ 37.85

Ⓑ 37.848

Ⓒ 37.846

Ⓓ 37.84

13 Order the following numbers from greatest to least.

729.614; 729.621; 729.612; 729.696

_____

14 Use < , >, or = to compare 29,468.92 and 29,468.29.

_____

15 Use <, >, or = to compare 18.39 and 18.390.

_____

14 Add and Subtract Decimals

WHAT IS THE SECRET WORD?

- Each letter in the problems represents a digit from 0 to 9. Use reasoning to find the digit that each letter represents. Record the letters to reveal a secret word. The letters for 4 and 9 are shown.

```
   O A P S          R E I D          A P S Z
 + E Z O S        -   Z O D        + Z D E Z
 ─────────        ─────────        ─────────
   R T D T D          S R T          D A E T
```

				E				S
0	1	2	3	4	5	6	7	8	9

 Turn and Talk

- How can you find the digit that the letter R represents without knowing any other digits?

- Which of the three problems could you use to find the digit for T?

- Explain how you found the digits represented by the other letters.

Are You Ready?

Complete these problems to review prior concepts and skills you will need for this module.

2-Digit Addition and Subtraction

Find the sum or difference.

1

	Tens	Ones
	☐	
	3	5
+	5	8

2

	Tens	Ones
	☐	☐
	6	4
−	3	9

Subtract Through 4-Digit Numbers: Subtract Across Zeros

Find the difference.

3
$$\begin{array}{r} 305 \\ -\ 56 \\ \hline \end{array}$$

4
$$\begin{array}{r} 500 \\ -\ 135 \\ \hline \end{array}$$

5
$$\begin{array}{r} 4{,}302 \\ -\ 233 \\ \hline \end{array}$$

6
$$\begin{array}{r} 2{,}006 \\ -\ 68 \\ \hline \end{array}$$

7
$$\begin{array}{r} 5{,}024 \\ -\ 876 \\ \hline \end{array}$$

8
$$\begin{array}{r} 1{,}507 \\ -\ 1{,}388 \\ \hline \end{array}$$

Place Value to Ten Thousand

Write the value of the underlined digit.

9 7<u>5</u>3 _____

10 <u>5</u>,875 _____

11 3,6<u>2</u>8 _____

12 5,<u>2</u>76 _____

13 2,73<u>5</u> _____

14 6,2<u>0</u>8 _____

Name
_____

Represent Decimal Addition

(**I Can**) use concrete models or drawings to represent decimal addition.

Spark Your Learning

A baker puts some flour onto a food scale as shown. What will the scale read if the baker adds another 0.29 pound of flour to the bowl?

Use a visual model to help you find the weight after the baker adds 0.29 pound of flour to the bowl. Draw to show your thinking.

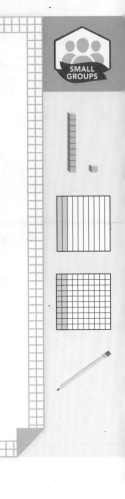

Turn and Talk How can you represent 0.4 in tenths and in hundredths? How did you represent tenths and hundredths in your visual model?

Build Understanding

1 What will the scale read if the baker adds another 0.8 pound of flour to the bowl?

Use base-ten blocks to help you find the weight after the baker adds the flour. Let one flat represent one whole and one long represent one tenth.

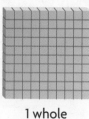

1 whole   1 tenth

A. Do you think the weight on the scale will be less than or greater than 1.0 pound? How do you know?

_____

_____

B. What base-ten blocks do you use to show 0.3 and 0.8?

_____

C. What do you get when you add the tenths?

_____

D. Do you need to regroup? Explain.

_____

E. What is the weight after the baker adds the flour to the bowl?

_____

 Turn and Talk How is adding decimals using base-ten blocks like adding whole numbers using base-ten blocks?

2 The baker puts dried fruit onto the food scale. The scale reads 1.86 pounds. What will the scale read if the baker adds another 1.28 pounds of dried fruit to the scale? Use quick pictures to help you find the answer.

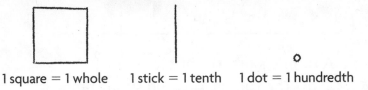

1 square = 1 whole   1 stick = 1 tenth   1 dot = 1 hundredth

A. Draw a quick picture to represent each weight.

B. How can you regroup the place values shown in your picture?

_____

C. Draw a quick picture to represent the total weight.

D. What is the weight of the dried fruit on the scale?

_____

 Turn and Talk When performing decimal addition, when and how do you regroup?

Check Understanding

1 At the store, Jo buys 0.8 pound of white mushrooms and 0.2 pound of brown mushrooms. How many pounds of mushrooms does she buy? Draw a visual model to find

your answer. _____

On Your Own

2 The digital caliper shows the width of a foreign coin as 25.75 millimeters. What is the combined width of two of these coins?

_____

3 (MP) **Attend to Precision** A runner's first sprint time for a 100-meter race is 10.76 seconds. The runner's second sprint time is 10.85 seconds. What is the combined time for the two sprints? Which place value(s) require regrouping?

_____

Add. Draw a visual model.

4 1.05 + 0.25 = _____

5 _____ = 0.74 + 0.4

6 (MP) **Use Tools** Use the decimal model to show the addition of 0.16 and 0.25. Explain how you used the decimal model.

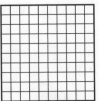

_____

_____

_____

✦ I'm in a Learning Mindset!

How can I make sure that my visual model represents the situation?

_____

_____

Name _____

Represent Decimal Subtraction

(I Can) use concrete models or drawings to represent
decimal subtraction.

Spark Your Learning

Adriana monitors the growth of a bamboo
cane. How much does the bamboo cane
grow from Day 5 to Day 9?

**Use a visual model to help you find
how much the bamboo cane grows.
Draw to show your thinking.**

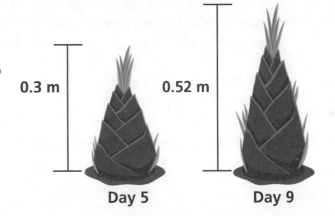

0.3 m

0.52 m

Day 5

Day 9

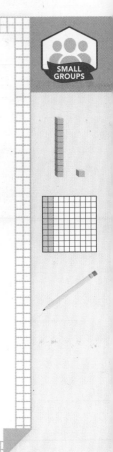

Turn and Talk After 13 days, the bamboo cane is 1.2 meters
tall. How would you adjust your visual model to find how
much the cane grows from Day 9 to Day 13?

Build Understanding

1 Nathan uses a piece of bamboo to make a bamboo flute. In order for his flute to play in the key of F, he needs the flute to be 0.4 meter long. How much does Nathan need to cut from his piece of bamboo?

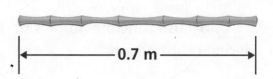

0.7 m

Use base-ten blocks to help you find how much Nathan needs to cut.

A. Is the length that he needs to cut less than or greater than 1.0 meter? How do you know?

_____

_____

_____

B. What base-ten blocks do you use to show 0.7 and 0.4?

_____

C. Describe how you can use your base-ten blocks to find how much Nathan needs to cut. Do you need to regroup? Explain.

_____

_____

_____

_____

D. How much does Nathan need to cut from his piece of bamboo? How does your answer compare to your answer from Part A?

_____

 Turn and Talk How does subtraction with decimals compare to subtraction with whole numbers?

2 Priya and Nathan compare the weights of their flutes. How much more does Priya's flute weigh than Nathan's flute?

Nathan's flute
2.75 ounces

Priya's flute
3.81 ounces

A. Draw a quick picture to represent the weight of Priya's flute.

B. How can you find how much more Priya's flute weighs? Draw to show your thinking.

C. Describe how you regrouped.

_____

_____

D. How much more does Priya's flute weigh than Nathan's flute?

_____

Check Understanding

1 Paula's kitten weighs 2.15 pounds. Ian's kitten weighs 3.32 pounds. How much more does Ian's kitten weigh? Draw a visual model to find your answer.

_____

On Your Own

3.65 lb

2 A recipe requires 5 pounds of apples. Marcel weighs his apples and does not have enough. How many more pounds of apples does he need?

_____

3 (MP) **Use Tools** Use the decimal model to show the difference 0.64 − 0.17.

What is the difference? _____

Subtract. Use base-ten blocks or a visual model.

4 0.9 − 0.2

5 6.4 − 3.3

6 8 − 6.99

_____ _____ _____

7 (MP) **Critique Reasoning** Billy claims that it is not necessary to regroup when subtracting 3.67 from 8.63. Is Billy correct? Explain your reasoning.

_____

_____

8 **Open Ended** How do you regroup during decimal subtraction?

_____

_____

_____

 I'm in a Learning Mindset!

How do I know that my visual model is correct?

_____

_____

© Houghton Mifflin Harcourt Publishing Company

Name _____

Assess Reasonableness of Sums and Differences

(I Can) use benchmarks or rounding to check the reasonableness of decimal sums and differences.

Spark Your Learning

Mr. Gilbert downloads two files onto his computer. The table shows the sizes of the two files. He says that he downloads about 2 megabytes of data.

File 1	1.27 megabytes
File 2	1.79 megabytes

Is Mr. Gilbert's statement reasonable? Justify your answer using a visual model.

SMALL GROUPS

 Turn and Talk How can you use rounding to check that an answer is reasonable?

Build Understanding

1 The table shows the sizes of two different video files. Ms. Lee says that she uses 0.22 gigabyte more for video file A than for video file B, and that she uses a total of 0.96 gigabyte for both video files.

Video File A	0.74 gigabyte
Video File B	0.52 gigabyte

A. Locate points on the number line to show the size of each video file.

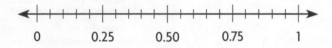

0   0.25   0.50   0.75   1

B. Which benchmarks on the number line can you use to estimate the size of each video file? How do you know?

_____

_____

_____

C. Is Ms. Lee's statement that she uses 0.22 gigabyte more for video file A than for video file B reasonable? Explain how you know.

_____

_____

D. Is Ms. Lee's statement that she uses a total of 0.96 gigabyte for both video files reasonable? Explain how you know.

_____

_____

 Turn and Talk How do these benchmarks compare to the benchmarks used in fractions?

© Houghton Mifflin Harcourt Publishing Company

Step It Out

2 The table shows a cellular phone provider's monthly charges for voice and data services. What is the difference in cost of voice and data services? Mr. Sanchez says that the difference is $23.23. Is his answer reasonable?

Voice Services	$12.72
Data Services	$35.95

A. Estimate the difference in cost by rounding each cost to the nearest ten dollars. Write an equation to support your answer.

_____

B. Estimate the difference in cost by rounding each cost to the nearest dollar. Write an equation to support your answer.

_____

C. Is Mr. Sanchez's answer reasonable? How do you know?

_____

Check Understanding

1 Use the table of cellular phone charges above. Is it reasonable to say that the cost of both services is about $40? Explain.

_____

_____

_____

2 Nancy buys 0.12 pound of black beans and 0.81 pound of pinto beans. She says she bought 0.69 pound more pinto beans than black beans. Is her statement reasonable? Explain how you know.

_____

_____

_____

On Your Own

3 In professional hockey, the record for the average number of points scored each game by a player is 1.92 points. The fourth best average number of points is 1.39 points. Is it reasonable to say that the difference in the average numbers of points is 0.53 point? Explain.

_____

_____

4 (MP) **Construct Arguments** Nicole buys the two small pizzas shown. Nicole says that the cost of both pizzas is about $20. Is her answer reasonable? Justify your answer.

$6.79

$9.29

_____

_____

_____

5 (MP) **Use Tools** Carson says that the difference of 0.73 and 0.45 is 0.28. Is Carson's answer reasonable? Justify your answer using the number line.

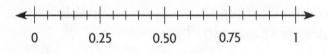

_____

_____

_____

✚× I'm in a Learning Mindset!
÷

What strategies can I use to assess reasonableness?

_____

Name _____

Add Decimals

(I Can) use a written method and strategies based on place value to add decimals.

Step It Out

1 Willem buys a whistle and a yo-yo for his niece. What is the total cost of the gifts?

Use the chart to help you find the cost.

A. Line up the place values of the two prices.

B. Add the hundredths.

C. Add the tenths. Do you need to regroup the tenths? Explain.

_____

_____

_____

D. Add the ones.

E. What is the cost of the two gifts? _____

F. How is the written method you used in your chart related to using base-ten blocks or quick pictures to add decimals?

_____

_____

_____

_____

Turn and Talk How is adding decimals like adding whole numbers?

Step It Out

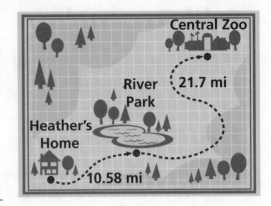

2 ▸ Heather and her mom drive from her home to River Park and then to Central Zoo as shown. How far do they drive?

A. Write an equation to estimate how far they drive.

_____

Use the chart to help you find how far they drive.

B. Line up the place values of the two distances.

C. What is 21.7 written to the hundredths place? _____

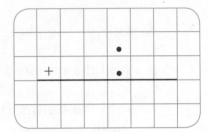

D. Add the hundredths first. Then, add the tenths, ones, and tens. Regroup as needed.

E. How far do they drive? Is your answer reasonable? How do you know?

_____

_____

 Turn and Talk Does the value of 21.7 change when you write a 0 in the hundredths place? Explain.

Check Understanding [Math Board]

1 Larry buys a pint of milk for $1.19 and a sandwich for $4.85. How much does Larry spend for the milk and sandwich? _____

Find the sum.

2 3.87 + 6.55

3 29.67 + 13.9

4 2.5 + 3.26 + 4.34

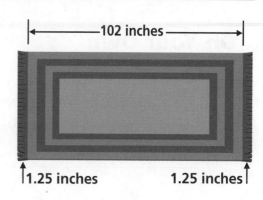

← 102 inches →

1.25 inches   1.25 inches

On Your Own

5 (MP) **Attend to Precision** A rug measures 102 inches long. It has fringe that measures 1.25 inches long on each end. What is the total length of the rug including the fringe on both ends?

_____

6 (MP) **Use Tools** Ms. Davis has been keeping track of the price of a new sweater that she wants to buy. The original price is $19.99. One week later, the price goes up by $1.50. Two weeks later, the price goes up by another $2. What is the price of the sweater two weeks later? Use the chart to find the price.

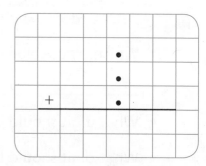

_____

Find the sum.

7 6.89 + 7.34

8 37.9 + 18.2

9 132.7 + 58.54

_____ _____ _____

10 15.76 + 8.2

11 6.87 + 5.18

12 19.7 + 5.46

_____ _____ _____

13 (MP) **Reason** After Andrew cleans a fish tank, it has 24.5 liters of water in it. He uses a container that holds 0.65 liter to add fresh water to the tank.

- How much water is in the fish tank after Andrew adds 2 containers of water? _____

- How much water is in the fish tank after Andrew adds 3 containers of water? _____

- The fish tank holds 30 liters. How many containers of water could Andrew add without overfilling the tank?

_____

On Your Own

14 (MP) **Reason** When Harvey was 10 years old, he was 48.5 inches tall. By age 20, he had grown another 21.75 inches. Was Harvey at least 6 feet tall by age 20? Explain.

_____

_____

15 (MP) **Attend to Precision** Layla adds 57.2, 38.35, and 46.19.

- Which place values require regrouping?

    _____

- What digit should be in the tenths place of Layla's sum? _____

- What digit should be in the ones place of Layla's sum? _____

Find the sum.

16 67.5 + 38.2

17 24.65 + 56.7

18 237.92 + 825.51

19 (MP) **Model with Mathematics** Jason measures the mass of a rock. The mass of the rock is the same as the combined mass of a 1.25-kilogram weight and a 2.5-kilogram weight. What is the mass of the rock? Write an equation to model the problem.

20 **Open Ended** Rita wants to explain to her friend how to add 13.6 and 5.95. What should Rita say?

_____

_____

_____

Name
_____

Subtract Decimals

(I Can) use a written method and strategies based on place
value to subtract decimals.

Step It Out

1 Santiago is at the store with his brother. He reads
the total for his purchase on the cash register and
realizes that he has only $4.73. His brother pays the
difference. How much does Santiago's brother pay?

Use the chart to help you solve the problem.

A. Write the numbers in the chart so that the lesser
number is subtracted from the greater number.
Line up the place values.

B. Subtract the hundredths. Regroup as needed.

C. Subtract the tenths. Regroup as needed.

D. Subtract the ones.

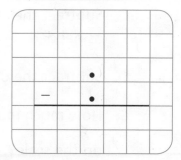

E. How much does Santiago's brother pay?

_____

F. How is the written method you used in your chart
related to using base-ten blocks or quick pictures
to subtract decimals?

_____

_____

_____

_____

  Turn and Talk How can you use the relationship between
addition and subtraction to check your answer?

© Houghton Mifflin Harcourt Publishing Company

Step It Out

 2 Ms. Gomez goes to the butcher shop to buy 17.5 ounces of chicken for her dinner party. She looks at the weight of the chicken that the butcher has put on the scale. How much more chicken does the butcher need to put on the scale?

Use the chart to help you solve the problem.

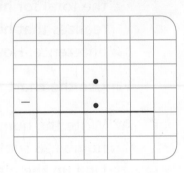

13.68 oz

A. Write the numbers in the chart so that the lesser number is subtracted from the greater number. Line up the place values.

B. What do you need to do to keep place values aligned when subtracting?

_____

C. Subtract the hundredths and the tenths. Regroup as needed.

D. Subtract the ones and tens. Regroup as needed.

E. How much more chicken does the butcher need to put

on the scale? _____

 Turn and Talk How can you determine whether your answer is reasonable?

Check Understanding `Math Board`

1 A bicycle costs $129.98. A man pays for the bike with $140.

How much change should he get back? _____

Find the difference.

2 8.5 − 6.7

3 32.4 − 19.52

4 76.5 − 57.42

_____ _____ _____

On Your Own

5 In 1984, a new Olympic record of 49.8 seconds was set for the men's 100-meter freestyle swim. At the 2016 Olympics, the winning time for this race was 2.22 seconds less than the 1984 Olympic record. What was the winning time in 2016?

_____

6 Val spends $16.37 at a store. She pays the sales clerk with a $20 bill and two quarters. How much change should

Val get back? _____

7 (MP) **Critique Reasoning** Omar finds the difference of 5,000 and 0.9 to be 4,991. Is he correct? If not, what is his error and what is the correct answer?

_____

_____

Find the difference.

8   0.60
       − 0.38

9   27.4
       − 9.13

10   34.6
       − 8.72

11 (MP) **Attend to Precision** In a relay race, athletes each run the same distance and carry a baton that is passed from one runner to the next. Emil's school is holding 3-person relay races for field day. Cassidy's time is 13.5 seconds. Emil's time is 13.87 seconds. Alejandro's time is 12.95 seconds.

• What is the team's time for the relay race?

_____

• How much faster is Cassidy's time than Emil's time?

_____

• How much faster is Alejandro's time than Cassidy's time?

_____

On Your Own

12 **Geography** In the Northern Hemisphere, the fall equinox marks the first day of fall. On this September day, day and night are each about 12 hours long. Then daylight shortens daily until the winter solstice in December. On September 22, 2018, Juneau, Alaska had about 734 minutes of daylight, and it began losing about 5.02 minutes of daylight each day.

- About how many minutes of daylight did Juneau have on September 25? Show your work.

_____

13 **Find the difference.**

- four and fifty-six hundredths
  subtracted from seven and thirty-eight hundredths _____

- two and eighty-four hundredths
  subtracted from six and five tenths _____

Find the difference.

14 $4.28 - 3.16$ **15** $27.64 - 16.98$ **16** $84.35 - 67.27$

_____   _____   _____

Find the unknown number.

17 $3.74 - 2.8 = \blacksquare$ **18** $1.7 = \blacksquare - 4.63$ **19** $21.3 - \blacksquare = 12.45$

_____   _____   _____

20 How can you use mental math to subtract 0.9 from 500?

_____

_____

_____

_____

Name _____

Use Strategies and Reasoning to Add and Subtract

(I Can) add and subtract decimals by using reasoning and strategies involving addition properties or friendly numbers.

Step It Out

1 Kyle finds two games that he wants to buy.

Video Game Prices	
Game	Price
Dark Embers	$15.97
Golden Scythe	$13.47

A. What amount does Kyle pay for the two games?

- Find friendly numbers. Add $0.03 to the price of Dark Embers. Subtract $0.03 from the price of Golden Scythe. What are the new prices?

  _____

- What is the cost for both games? _____

- Is this the same as 15.97 + 13.47? How do you know?

  _____

  _____

B. How much more does Dark Embers cost than Golden Scythe?

- Find friendly numbers. Subtract 0.47 from the price of each

  game. What are the new prices? _____

- What is the difference in price? _____

- Is this the same as 15.97 − 13.47? How do you know?

  _____

  _____

 Turn and Talk How could you find the sum and difference in a different way?

Step It Out

2 Kyle wants to buy three accessories for his club's gaming system. He writes 32.75 + 11.98 + 24.25 to find the total cost.

Gaming System Accessories	
Accessory	**Price**
Controller	$32.75
Racing Wheel	$11.98
Headset	$24.25

A. Kyle notices that 0.75 and 0.25 from the first and third addends have a sum of 1.00. He uses the Commutative Property of Addition and the Associative Property of Addition to regroup the addends to add them first.

$(32.75 + 11.98) + 24.25 = 32.75 + (11.98 + 24.25)$ Associative Property

$= 32.75 + (24.25 + 11.98)$ Commutative Property

$= (32.75 + 24.25) + 11.98$ Associative Property

Rewrite the sum as an expression with two addends. _____

B. What is the cost of all three accessories? _____

 Turn and Talk Explain why addition properties can make solving an addition problem easier than using friendly numbers.

Check Understanding [Math Board]

1 Use the table above to write and solve an equation to find how much more a headset costs than a racing wheel. How can using friendly numbers help you?

_____

_____

Add or subtract. Explain what strategy you used.

2 27.86 + 31.44 + 12.14

3 79.32 − 42.05

On Your Own

4 (MP) **Reason** At the department store, Ms. Jarvis finds two winter coats that she likes. What is the cost to buy both coats? Explain your reasoning.

$48.98

$34.56

_____

_____

_____

5 (MP) **Critique Reasoning** Ina claims she can find 58.42 − 16.95 by solving the equation 58.47 − 17.00 = n. Is she correct? Justify your reasoning.

_____

Add or subtract.

6 37.41 − 29.08

_____

7 437.60 − 321.75

_____

8 138.62 + 567.88 + 319.38

_____

9 817.62 − 408.03

_____

10 The table shows the price of some school supplies.

- How much more do pencils cost than a notebook?

_____

- What is the cost to buy one package each of erasers, paper clips, and pencils? _____

- How much do three notebooks cost? _____

- Describe how you can use friendly numbers to find how much more pencils cost than paper clips.

_____

_____

School Supplies	
Item	Price
Notebook	$1.29
Erasers	$1.30
Paper clips	$1.56
Pencils	$1.71

On Your Own

11 The dimensions of a polygon are given.

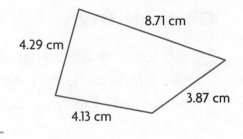

8.71 cm

4.29 cm

3.87 cm

4.13 cm

- What is the perimeter of the polygon?

_____

- How much longer is the
longest side than the shortest side? _____

12 (MP) **Use Structure** Yuan is given the following problem.

$$37.5 + (15.32 + 12.5)$$

- How can Yuan use the Commutative Property of Addition and
the Associative Property of Addition to simplify the problem?

_____

_____

_____

- How can he use friendly numbers to simplify the problem?

_____

_____

- What is the sum? _____

13 Margot has $21.50 to spend at the street fair. She buys roasted
peanuts for $4.75 and a hot dog for $2.99. How much money

does she have left? _____

14 **Open Ended** When is it better to use friendly numbers to solve
a decimal addition problem, and when is it better to use the
properties of addition to solve?

_____

_____

_____

Review

Concepts and Skills

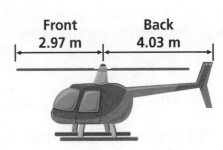

Front
2.97 m

Back
4.03 m

The lengths of the front and back of a helicopter are shown. Use the diagram for 1–3.

1 What is the length of the helicopter?

_____

2 (MP) **Use Tools** What is a reasonable estimate for the difference between the lengths of the front and back of the helicopter? Tell what strategy or tool you will use to answer the question, explain your choice, and then find the answer.

_____

3 What is the difference in the lengths of the front and back of the helicopter?

_____

4 Select all the expressions that have the same value as 3.75 − 2.63.

(A) 4 − 2.38   (D) (3 − 2) − (0.75 − 0.63)

(B) 4 − 2.88   (E) (3 − 2) + (0.75 − 0.63)

(C) 3 − 1.88

5 Use the chart to subtract 5.64 from 11.35.

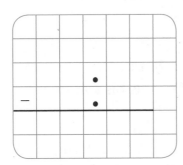

What is the difference? _____

6 Use the chart to add 28.4 and 9.38.

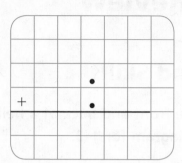

What is the sum? _____

7 Which represents the sum 1.3 + 0.46?

(A) 1.76   (B) 1.94   (C) 5.36   (D) 5.9

8 How would you explain to someone how to subtract 3.85 from 9.2? What is the difference?

_____

_____

9 Select all the expressions that have a value of 28.02.

(A) 13.75 + 14.27

(B) 13.75 + 14.25 + 0.02

(C) 13.78 + 14.30

(D) 13.78 + 14.30 + 0.03

(E) 27 + 1 + 0.02

10 Joe's rabbit weighs 1.35 pounds. Dale's rabbit weighs 0.68 pound. How much more does Joe's rabbit weigh?

_____

11 Carlos buys 0.19 pound of basmati rice and 0.78 pound of brown rice. He says that he bought 1.97 pounds of rice. Is his statement reasonable? Explain.

_____

_____

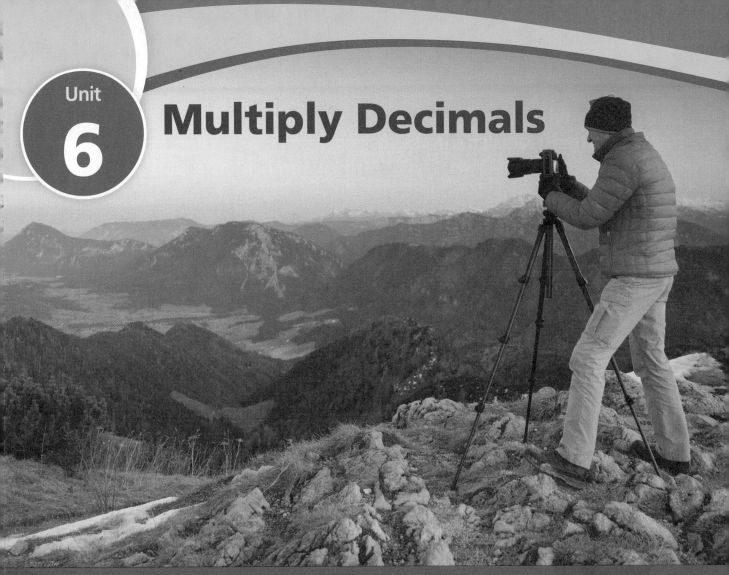

Unit 6

Multiply Decimals

Photographer

Photographers can work practically anywhere in the world, including underwater. Some work inside studios, while others prefer to capture the natural world outside. You can even find photographers working at special events like weddings and graduations.

Did you know that photographers work with news organizations so you can not only read about events, but see pictures that go along with the stories?

Professional photographers are artists, and sometimes their photos are displayed in museums.

STEM Task:

Photographers take time to compose their photos. Take a piece of sturdy paper and cut out a rectangle so that it looks like a picture frame. Find something in your classroom that would be a good subject for a photo. Then hold up the paper to frame the object. Move the frame closer or farther away or view the object from different angles. For example, place a cone or other shape somewhere where it casts a shadow. Observe the changes to the shadow as you move the frame. Draw what you see.

Learning Mindset
Perseverance Learns Effectively

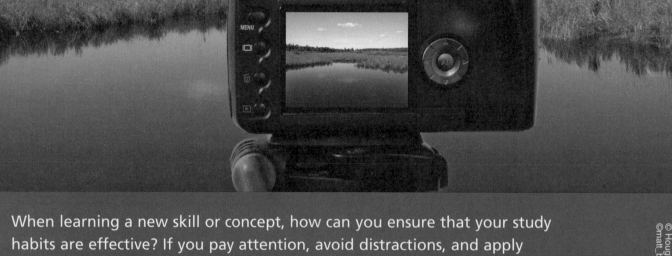

When learning a new skill or concept, how can you ensure that your study habits are effective? If you pay attention, avoid distractions, and apply organizational skills, you are more likely to understand and remember what you've been learning. One way to help your memory is to take notes shortly after learning something. Writing what you learned in your own words helps it stick in your memory.

Reflect

Q When working on the STEM Task, how were you able to keep yourself from getting distracted?

Q Did you take the time to develop a plan for your learning? What was effective when you were finding the right angle to frame the object?

Multiply Decimals and Whole Numbers

Which snail wins the race?

- Suppose each snail finishes the race by moving the distance shown in one hour. Which snails will complete the remainder of the race in 7 hours or less?

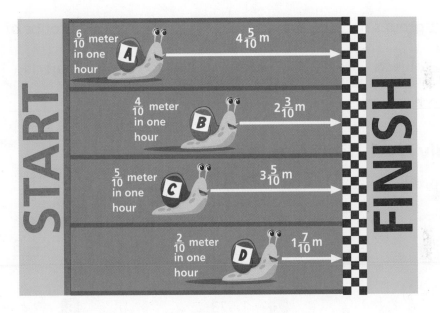

- Which snails will complete the remainder of the race in 7 hours or less?

_____

- Which snail will be the winner?

_____

 Turn and Talk

- How did you solve the problem?

Are You Ready?

Complete these problems to review prior concepts and skills you will need for this module.

Count Equal Groups

Count equal groups to find the total.

 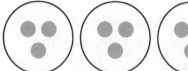

_____ groups of _____ objects

_____ objects

_____ groups of _____ objects

_____ objects

Multiply by 1-Digit Numbers

Find the product.

3   67
      × 8

4   43
      × 7

5   654
      × 3

6   945
      × 4

7   1,573
      ×   5

8   2,432
      ×   6

Multiply with 3-Digit Numbers

Find the product.

9   435
      × 86

10   283
       × 52

11   167
       × 24

Name

Understand Decimal Multiplication Patterns

(I Can) **multiply decimals by powers of 10 that are both greater than and less than 1.**

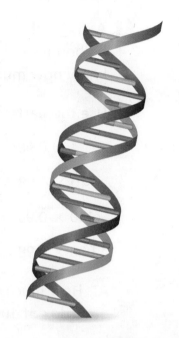

Spark Your Learning

DNA is the genetic code that determines many of your traits. It is found rolled up inside your body's cells. Uncoiled, each strand of DNA is 71.0 inches long. This measurement is equivalent to about 1.8 meters. What is the length of 10 uncoiled DNA strands placed end-to-end in inches and in meters?

Show your thinking.

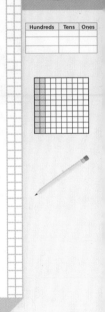

Hundreds	Tens	Ones

Turn and Talk In each instance, what happens to the place-value positions of the digits and the placement of the decimal point?

Build Understanding

1 A discount store sells all items for $0.98 each. Items can be bought in boxes of 10, 100, or 1,000. Jolene wants to know how much each box will cost.

ALL ITEMS
$0.98 EACH

Use the pattern to answer the questions.

$1 \times 0.98 = 0.98$

$10 \times 0.98 = 9.8$

$100 \times 0.98 = 98$

$1,000 \times 0.98 = 980$

A. How much will it cost to buy 1 box of 10 items? 1 box of 100 items? 1 box of 1,000 items?

_____

B. What is the value of the digit 9 in 0.98? in 9.80? in 98? in 980?

_____

C. In which direction do the digits shift as you multiply by increasing powers of 10?

_____

D. How does the shifting of the digits affect the position of the decimal point as you multiply by increasing powers of 10?

_____

_____

E. Show the movement of the decimal point in the pattern above.

 Turn and Talk If you multiply a number by 100, how will the placement of the decimal point change? Find at least two ways in which the pattern above shows that this is true.

2 Mrs. Gymni sells jump ropes on her website for $2.35 each. She sold 10^2 jump ropes last week. How much did she earn?

A. Complete the pattern.

$10^0 \times 2.35 =$ _____

$10^1 \times 2.35 =$ _____

$10^2 \times 2.35 =$ _____

$10^3 \times 2.35 =$ _____

B. Which equation shows 2.35 multiplied by 10 once?

_____

- Write this equation using a factor of 10.

_____

- How does the placement of the decimal point in the product compare to its placement in 2.35?

_____

C. Which equation shows 2.35 multiplied by 10

three times? _____

- Write this equation using factors of 10.

_____

- How does the placement of the decimal point in the product compare to its placement in 2.35?

_____

D. How much did Mrs. Gymni earn last week from selling 10^2 jump ropes?

_____

 Turn and Talk How does the change in the position of the decimal point relate to the exponent on the 10?

Build Understanding

3 The first-place finisher in a magazine drive raised $935 in sales. Most participants raised $\frac{1}{10}$ of that amount. The least amount raised was $\frac{1}{100}$ of that amount.

Use the pattern to answer the questions.

$1 \times 935 = 935$

$0.1 \times 935 = 93.5$

$0.01 \times 935 = 9.35$

A. What is the value of the digit 5 in 935? in 93.5? in 9.35?

_____

B. How do the digits shift as you multiply by 1, 0.1, and 0.01?

_____

_____

C. How does the shifting of the digits affect the position of the decimal point as you multiply by 1, 0.1, and 0.01?

_____

_____

D. How much did most participants raise? _____

How much was the least amount raised? _____

Check Understanding

Chromosome 13 in the human body contains a DNA molecule that is about 3.19 centimeters long.

1 What is the length of 1,000 of these molecules? _____

2 What is the combined length of 10^2 of these molecules? _____

3 What is 0.1 of the length of chromosome 13? _____

On Your Own

4 **STEM** The length of a single DNA molecule is 3.4 nanometers. What is the combined length of 100 DNA molecules?

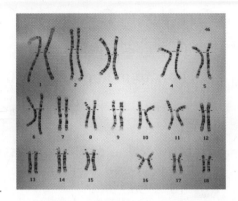

_____

Find the value of the expression.

5 $10^2 \times 38{,}256.77$

_____

6 100×932.56

_____

7 $0.01 \times 7{,}143.5$

_____

8 $1{,}000 \times 42.35$

_____

9 $10^3 \times 5{,}976$

_____

10 $0.1 \times 3{,}654$

_____

Find the value that makes the equation true.

11 $10^3 \times \blacksquare = 34{,}000$

_____

12 $843 = 100 \times \blacksquare$

_____

13 $0.01 \times \blacksquare = 76.55$

_____

14 An author sells books on a website for $8.95 each.

• A teacher orders 10 books. How much will the teacher pay?

_____

• A library orders 10^3 books. How much will the library pay?

_____

Complete the pattern.

15 $0.01 \times 72.3 =$ _____

$0.1 \times 72.3 =$ _____

$1 \times 72.3 =$ _____

$10 \times 72.3 =$ _____

16 $10^0 \times 3.58 =$ _____

$10^1 \times 3.58 =$ _____

$10^2 \times 3.58 =$ _____

$10^3 \times 3.58 =$ _____

On Your Own

17 (MP) **Attend to Precision** How would you explain to another student how to multiply 725 by 0.01?

_____

Find the value of the expression.

18 10 × 565.54

19 0.01 × 9,764.6

20 10^3 × 76.34

_____

Find the value that makes the equation true.

21 10 × ■ = 4,276.4

22 0.1 × ■ = 7,354

23 10^3 × ■ = 78,660

_____

24 Four different boxes weigh a total of 245 pounds.

- One box weighs $\frac{1}{10}$ of the total amount. How much does this box weigh? _____

- Another box weighs $\frac{1}{100}$ of the total amount. How much does this box weigh? _____

Complete the pattern.

25 10^0 × 345.89 = _____

10^1 × 345.89 = _____

10^2 × 345.89 = _____

10^3 × 345.89 = _____

26 10 × 144.2 = _____

1 × 144.2 = _____

0.1 × 144.2 = _____

0.01 × 144.2 = _____

⬡ I'm in a Learning Mindset!

What do I do when I'm learning something new? What helps me remember what to do?

_____

Name

Represent Multiplication with Decimals and Whole Numbers

(**I Can**) represent the product of a decimal less than one and a whole number using a visual model.

Spark Your Learning

Mary is shopping at the grocery store. She finds the weight of one banana and buys two more bananas that weigh the same amount. What is the weight of the 3 bananas?

0.28 pound

Justify your thinking.

Turn and Talk How can you model the situation with an equation? Compare your equation with a classmate.

Build Understanding

1 A starfish moves slowly in the ocean. Its speed is about 0.2 mile each hour. How many miles can a starfish travel in 4 hours?

Use the decimal model to find the distance.

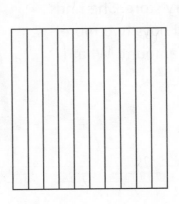

A. How did you use the decimal model to represent the distance traveled in one hour?

_____

B. How did you use the decimal model to represent the distance traveled in 4 hours?

_____

C. How can you model the solution with an addition expression?

_____

D. How can you model the solution with a multiplication expression?

_____

E. How many miles does a starfish travel in 4 hours?

_____

2 Adam weighs 6 apples. If each apple weighs 0.34 pound, what is the weight of the 6 apples?

??? pounds

A. Write a multiplication expression to model the situation. _____

B. Draw a quick picture to represent the problem.

C. How many hundredths are there? How do you regroup them?

_____

D. How many tenths are there? How do you regroup them?

_____

E. What is the weight of the 6 apples? _____

 Turn and Talk How is regrouping decimals similar to and different from regrouping whole numbers?

• •

Check Understanding

1 Kinshasa buys 2 peppers. Each pepper weighs 0.37 pound. What

is the weight of the peppers? _____

Multiply. Use a visual model.

2 4 × 0.24 = _____

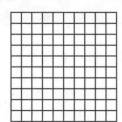

3 3 × 0.4 = _____

On Your Own

4 **Model with Mathematics** A square photo has a side length of 0.17 foot. The photo is enlarged by doubling the dimensions. Then it is enlarged again by tripling the new dimensions. Write equations to model each enlargement. What are the side lengths of the enlarged photo?

_____

5 Baby opossums are so tiny that a teaspoon can hold an entire litter. The mass of one baby opossum is 0.13 gram. What is the mass of a litter of 9 baby opossums?

_____

Multiply. Use a decimal model.

6 $2 \times 0.47 =$ _____

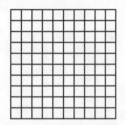

7 _____ $= 3 \times 0.6$

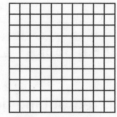

8 Use a visual model to find 7×0.43.

$7 \times 0.43 =$ _____

⬡ I'm in a Learning Mindset!

Was using a visual model effective in helping me understand multiplication with decimals? Explain why or why not.

_____

Name _____

Assess Reasonableness of Products

(I Can) assess the reasonableness of the product of a decimal less than one and a whole number.

Spark Your Learning

Rosalind's school is holding a Math Fun Fair. One of the games is a sorting game with the numerical expressions shown.

8×0.45 8×0.6 6×0.81 8×0.52

8×0.8 4×0.99 8×0.49 4×0.9

Sort the numerical expressions.

SMALL GROUPS

Greater than 4	Less than 4

Turn and Talk How does the value of the expression 8×0.45 compare to the value of the expression 4×0.99? Explain how you know.

Build Understanding

1 One of the prizes at the Math Fun Fair is erasers. The value of each eraser is $0.77. There are 8 erasers on the prize table. Joni says the value of the 8 erasers is greater than $6.00. How is she able to make this claim? Is her claim reasonable?

A. Did Joni give an exact value or an **estimate** for the 8 erasers?

_____

B. Decimals and fractions both name fractional parts of a whole. It is often easier to calculate using fractions rather than decimals. Complete the number line to show the decimal equivalents of some common fractions.

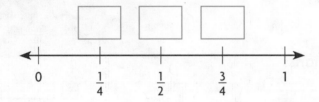

C. To which decimal number is $0.77 closest? _____

D. What fraction is equivalent to 0.75? _____

E. Use the fraction to find the value of the 8 erasers. Show your work.

_____

F. How does 0.77 compare to 0.75?

_____

G. Is Joni's claim reasonable? Explain.

_____

_____

 Turn and Talk What would the value of one eraser need to be so that the value of 8 erasers would be greater than or equal to $2.00 and less than or equal to $4.00?

Name _____

Step It Out

2 At another Math Fun Fair booth, a player chooses a digit from 1 to 9, spins the wheel, and multiplies the two numbers. If the product is greater than or equal to the digit, the player wins a prize.

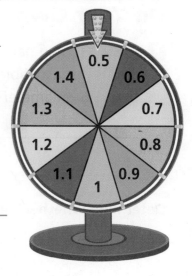

A. Taylor chooses the digit 4 and spins the number 0.7. Does she win a prize? How do you know?

_____

B. Is there any digit Taylor could have chosen for which a spin of 0.7 results in her winning a prize? Why?

_____

_____

C. For what other numbers on the wheel will Taylor not win

a prize? _____

D. Which numbers on the wheel will result in Taylor winning

a prize? _____

 Turn and Talk Suppose the numbers on the wheel change. How can you tell whether a player will win a prize or not win a prize?

• •

Check Understanding

1 There are also 4 sticker packs on the prize table. The value of each is $0.46. Javier claims that the total value is less than $2.00. Is his claim reasonable? Explain.

_____

Determine whether the statement is _true_ or _false_.

2 $6 \times 0.52 < 3$ **3** $4 \times 0.61 > 2$ **4** $7 \times 0.87 > 7$

_____   _____   _____

On Your Own

5 **STEM** Human hair grows about 0.43 millimeter each day. Is it reasonable to expect that hair grows more than 3.5 millimeters in one week? Explain.

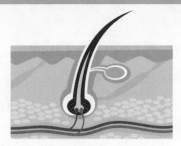

_____

_____

Determine whether the statement is *true* or *false*.

6 $2 \times 0.51 > 1$

7 $4 \times 0.49 > 2$

8 $5 \times 0.97 > 5$

_____   _____   _____

9 Jan goes to the grocery store to buy apples and oranges.

- Jan buys 5 apples. Is it reasonable that the apples weigh less than 5 pounds? Explain how you know.

  _____

  _____

0.74 lb

- Jan buys 6 oranges. Is it reasonable that the oranges weigh less than 3 pounds? Explain how you know.

  _____

  _____

0.55 lb

10 **(MP)** **Reason** Suppose you multiply 4 and 0.■7. What are the possible values of the unknown digit if the product is less than 1? Explain.

_____

_____

 I'm in a Learning Mindset!

What strategies do I use to stay on task?

_____

Name _____

Multiply Decimals by 1-Digit Whole Numbers

(I Can) multiply a decimal by a 1-digit whole number using the Distributive Property, partial products, and an area model.

Step It Out

1 Oceanographers recently discovered a new species of sea sponge in the Pacific Ocean. Sponges are animals, not plants, and can be found in both seawater and freshwater. Some sponges are able to move about 2.5 millimeters each day. How far might a sponge move in one week?

A. Write a numerical expression to model the situation. _____

B. What do the factors in your expression represent?

_____

_____

C. You can use the **Distributive Property** to multiply.

- Break apart 2.5 by place value. | $7 \times 2.5 = 7 \times ($ _____ $+$ _____ $)$

- Apply the Distributive Property. | $= 7 \times$ _____ $+ 7 \times$ _____

- What is the first product? | $=$ _____ $+ 7 \times$ _____

- What is the second product? | $=$ _____ $+$ _____

- Add the two products. | $=$ _____

D. How far might a sponge move in one week? _____

Turn and Talk How can you tell that your answer is reasonable?

Step It Out

2 ▶ The current rise in sea level is generally thought to be caused by the melting of ice sheets and glaciers. Scientists **estimate** that the rise in sea level is about 3.2 millimeters each year. What is the expected rise in sea level after 8 years?

A. What expression models the situation?

_____

B. What is an estimate for the rise in sea level after 8 years?

_____

C. Multiply by showing partial products.

- First multiply the 2 tenths by 8.

  8 × 2 tenths = _____ tenths, or

  _____ one _____ tenths

- Then multiply the 3 ones by 8.

  8 × 3 ones = _____ ones, or

  _____ tens _____ ones

- Add the partial products.

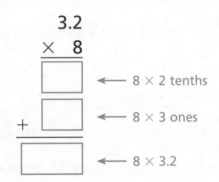

$$\begin{array}{r} 3.2 \\ \times\ \ 8 \\ \hline \end{array}$$

⟵ 8 × 2 tenths

⟵ 8 × 3 ones

⟵ 8 × 3.2

D. What is the expected rise in sea level after 8 years? How do you know your answer is reasonable?

_____

_____

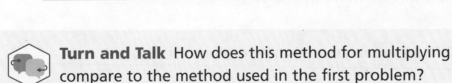

Turn and Talk How does this method for multiplying compare to the method used in the first problem?

3 Coral reefs grow about 1.25 centimeters each year. About how many centimeters does a coral reef grow in 9 years?

To solve, find 9 × 1.25. Use an area model to find the product.

A. Complete the area model.

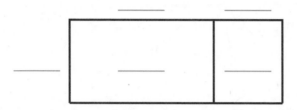

B. Add the areas of the two sections. What is the sum?

_____

C. About how much does a coral reef grow in 9 years?

_____

 Turn and Talk Compare the methods used to solve the problems in Tasks 2 and 3. Are they similar or different? Explain.

Check Understanding

1 A fisherman has 6 Atlantic mackerels. Each mackerel weighs

1.78 pounds. What is the weight of the 6 fish? _____

Multiply.

2
$$\begin{array}{r} 8.6 \\ \times\ \ 3 \\ \hline \end{array}$$

3
$$\begin{array}{r} 21.37 \\ \times\ \ \ \ 5 \\ \hline \end{array}$$

4
$$\begin{array}{r} 7.93 \\ \times\ \ 8 \\ \hline \end{array}$$

On Your Own

5 **(MP) Use Tools** Another type of sponge moves about
1.8 millimeters in 1 day. How far will this sponge move
in 4 days? Use an area model.

_____

Use the table for 6–9.

Weights of Different Species of Salmon	
Type of Salmon	Weight (pounds)
Atlantic	57.3
Sockeye	9.37
Chum	19.58
Pink	8.2

6 Albert catches 7 chum salmon. What is the weight

of the fish he catches? _____

7 From the fish market, a restaurant buys 5 whole
Atlantic salmon. What is the weight of the fish the

restaurant buys? _____

8 **(MP) Attend to Precision** Kerri and Jeff catch 3 sockeye
salmon and 6 pink salmon. What is the weight of the

fish they catch? _____

9 **Open Ended** Write and solve a problem that compares the
weights of two types of salmon.

_____

_____

_____

Multiply.

10   9.38
      × 2

11   0.76
      × 6

12   24.59
      × 9

© Houghton Mifflin Harcourt Publishing Company

Name _____

Use the prices shown for 13–16.

| Potatoes | Tomatoes | Onions | Broccoli |
| $1.65 each pound | $0.79 each pound | $1.29 each pound | $2.45 each pound |

13 Anna buys 3 pounds of potatoes. How much does she pay?

_____

14 Describe how you found the cost for 3 pounds of potatoes.

_____

_____

_____

15 Nicole buys 2 pounds of onions and 4 pounds of tomatoes. How much does she pay?

_____

16 Juan buys 3 pounds of onions and 2 pounds of broccoli. Raj buys 5 pounds of potatoes. Who pays more? Explain.

_____

_____

Use the table for 17–18.

17 What is the cost for 5 pounds of peanuts and 7 pounds of almonds?

_____

18 How much more do 3 pounds of cashews cost than 9 pounds of almonds?

_____

Nuts	Cost for each Pound
Peanuts	$1.25
Almonds	$2.75
Cashews	$11.50

On Your Own

19 A package of cheese contains eight slices. The scale shows the weight for one slice. What is the weight of the cheese in the package? Describe how you found the answer.

1.08 oz

_____

_____

_____

20 **Geography** During the 1962 Nor'easter, tides in Norfolk, Virginia reached 9 feet. At Canada's Bay of Fundy, tides can reach heights that are 5.89 times as great. What is the maximum height of the Bay of Fundy's tides?

_____

21 (MP) **Reason** When multiplying a decimal by a whole number, how do you decide where to put the decimal point?

_____

_____

_____

22 (MP) **Model with Mathematics** At the movies, adult tickets cost $8.50 and child tickets cost $6.75. How much does it cost 2 adults and 3 children to see a movie? Write and solve an equation to model this situation.

_____

23 **Open Ended** What method would you use to multiply 9.38 and 5? Explain your choice.

_____

_____

_____

Name _____

Multiply Decimals by 2-Digit Whole Numbers

(I Can) use an area model and place-value patterns to multiply a decimal by a 2-digit whole number.

Step It Out

1 ▸ When Sierra gets home from school each day, she drinks a 0.47-liter container of water. Find the amount of water Sierra drinks in 26 days.

A. To solve, find 26 × 0.47. Write each factor in expanded form.

_____

B. Use the rectangle to make an area model to represent the problem. Think about how to divide the sections using the expanded form of the factors. Find the partial products by finding the area of each section.

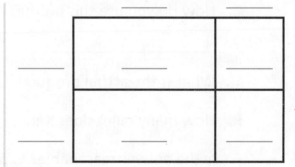

C. Arrange the partial products to find the sum.

D. How much water does Sierra drink in 26 days?

_____

0.47
× 26

20 × 0.4 ⟶ ☐

20 × 0.07 ⟶ ☐

6 × 0.4 ⟶ ☐

6 × 0.07 ⟶ ☐
+ _____
☐

 Turn and Talk Is your answer reasonable? Explain.

© Houghton Mifflin Harcourt Publishing Company • Image Credit: ©Digital Vision/Creative Crop/Getty Images

Step It Out

2 Kennard rides his bike 3.25 miles each day to get to and from school for the first 34 days of school. How many miles does he ride in those 34 days?

To solve, find 34 × 3.25. Use place-value patterns to find the product using whole numbers.

A. The factor 34 is a whole number. Multiply 3.25 by 100 to make it into a whole number.

What is the whole number? _____

B. Find the product of the whole numbers.

_____

C. How do you use this product to find the actual product?

_____

D. What is the actual product? _____

E. How many miles does Kennard ride? _____

F. Is the answer reasonable? Explain.

_____

_____

 Turn and Talk Jared rides his bike 2.8 miles each day to get to and from school. Explain how you can use place-value patterns to find 34 × 2.8.

Check Understanding

1 The distance around a field is 0.28 mile. If Anya runs around the field 12 times, how many miles does she run? Draw an area model to find

the answer. _____

© Houghton Mifflin Harcourt Publishing Company • Image Credit: ©LJSPhotography/Alamy

On Your Own

2 Every minute, 6.8 gallons of water flow from a garden hose into a pool. Find the amount of water in the pool after 32 minutes.

• Draw an area model.

• How much water is in the pool? _____

• Is your answer reasonable? Explain how you know.

_____

_____

Multiply. Show your work.

3 2.3
  $\times$ 14

4 0.58
  $\times$ 23

5 24.1
  $\times$ 82

6 (MP) **Critique Reasoning** Antoine multiplies 4.78 by 35 and says the product is 16.73. How do you know that Antoine is incorrect? What is the correct answer?

_____

_____

_____

_____

On Your Own

Use the table for 7–9.

The table shows the prices for different items at a used bookstore.

Hal's Bookstore	
Item	**Price**
Magazine	$0.65
Paperback book	$2.79
Hardback book	$5.40

7 On Monday, the store sells 28 hardback books. How much does the store earn? _____

8 On Tuesday, the store sells 63 paperback books and 34 magazines. How much does the store earn? _____

9 On Wednesday, the store sells 52 paperback books and 27 hardback books. Does the store earn more from the paperback books or the hardback books? Explain.

_____

_____

10 (MP) **Use Structure** The product 23 × 589 equals 13,547.

- Explain how you can use the product to find the value of the expression 23 × 58.9.

_____

_____

- Explain how you can use the product to find the value of the expression 23 × 5.89.

_____

_____

Name _____

Solve Problems Using Bar Models

(I Can) use a bar model to solve a multistep problem that uses multiplication.

Step It Out

1 The table shows the mass, in grams, of two different balls. What is the combined mass of 2 baseballs and 3 softballs?

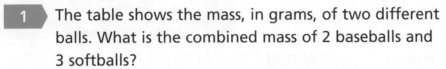

Type of Ball	Ball Weight (grams)
Baseball	141.75
Softball	198.45

Use a bar model to represent the problem.

A. Draw a bar model that shows the mass of 2 baseballs.

- Label each bar.

- What is the mass of 2 baseballs?

  _____

B. Draw a bar model that shows the mass of 3 softballs.

- Label each bar.

- What is the mass of 3 softballs?

  _____

C. Draw a bar model to show the combined mass of the 2 baseballs and 3 softballs.

D. What is the mass of 2 baseballs and 3 softballs?

  _____

Turn and Talk How would your bar model change if you were to compare the masses of 2 baseballs and 3 softballs?

Step It Out

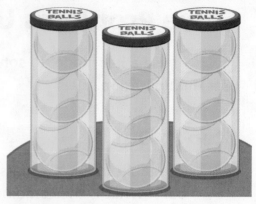

2 Shamir goes to the sporting goods store. He buys 3 cans of tennis balls. Each can costs $3.87. Shamir pays for his purchase with a $20 bill. How much change should the sales clerk give him?

Use a bar model to represent the problem.

A. Draw a bar model that shows the cost of 3 cans of tennis balls. Label each bar.

B. What is the cost of the three cans of tennis balls?

_____

C. Draw a bar model that compares the cost of three cans of tennis balls to $20. Label each bar.

D. How much change should the sales clerk give to Shamir? Explain how you know.

_____

_____

 Turn and Talk How do bar models help you to identify what operations to use?

Check Understanding

Use the table and make a bar model for 1 and 2.

Type of Ball	Weight (in ounces)
Golf ball	1.62
Volleyball	9.55

1 What is the combined weight of 1 volleyball and 3 golf balls?

_____

2 How much more do 2 volleyballs weigh than 9 golf balls?

_____

On Your Own

Make a bar model to solve.

3 A giraffe can cover one mile in about 6.4 minutes. An elephant can cover one mile in about 8.2 minutes. About how much longer will it take the elephant to cover 3 miles than the giraffe?

_____

On Your Own

Use a bar model for 4–6.

4 The mass of a baseball is 141.75 grams. The mass of a basketball is 623.7 grams. How much greater is the mass of a basketball than the mass of 3 baseballs?

5 Jenny gets paid $12.25 per hour. She worked 6 hours this week. How much more does she need to earn to have a total of $100?

6 Juanita buys 4 bags of red mulch, 1 bag of brown mulch, and a 3.25-pound bag of potting soil. If a bag of red mulch weighs 8.5 pounds and a bag of brown mulch weighs 6.75 pounds, what is the weight of Juanita's purchases?

Review

Vocabulary

1 Think about the steps to multiply 0.64 and 7. Draw lines to complete the sentence with the correct term.

Break apart 0.64 as
0.6 + 0.04 by using   •   • the Distributive Property.

Find the product
7 × (0.6 + 0.04) using   •   • partial products.

The expressions
7 × 0.6 and 7 × 0.04 are   •   • place values.

Concepts and Skills

2 Nicole multiplies 7,846.512 and 10^2. Between which two digits in the product should the decimal point be placed?

(A) 4 and 6

(C) 5 and 1

(B) 8 and 4

(D) 1 and 2

3 Select all the numbers that result in a product greater than 3 when multiplied by 6.

(A) 0.25

(C) 0.49

(E) 0.64

(B) 0.38

(D) 0.51

(F) 0.75

4 (MP) **Use Tools** Tobias helps his aunt repaint her shed. He works for 3 hours and earns $6.35 each hour. Tobias buys a bottle of water for $2.25 on his way home. How much money should he have left? Tell what strategy or tool you will use to answer the question, explain your choice, and then find the answer.

_____

_____

5 Lucinda buys 4 heads of cauliflower that weigh 1.88 pounds each. She buys 1 bag of potatoes that weighs 4.5 pounds. What is the weight of Lucinda's vegetable purchases? Use a bar model to solve.

How much do the vegetables weigh? _____

Multiply.

6 3 × 0.28

7 8 × 0.76

8 2 × (8.67 × 9)

_____   _____   _____

9 Janice buys 12 avocados. Each avocado costs $0.79. How much does Janice pay?

_____

10 Every minute, 1.8 gallons of water flow from a faucet. How many gallons of water flow from the faucet in 16 minutes?

_____

11 Benny and Kapri must earn 0.78 or more of the possible 400 points to pass their bicycle safety class. Benny says they need to earn more than 300 points to pass. Kapri says they can earn fewer than 300 points and still pass. Who is correct? Explain your reasoning.

_____

_____

_____

WHO CAN BUY A TICKET?

Four friends want to see a show. Each friend brings
a bag full of coins to pay for a ticket. A ticket
costs $20. (Hint: $20 = 2,000 cents)

- Which of the friends has enough money to buy a ticket?

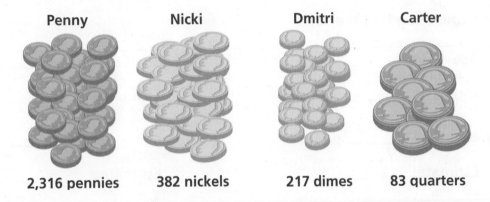

Penny	Nicki	Dmitri	Carter
2,316 pennies	382 nickels	217 dimes	83 quarters

 Turn and Talk

- How do you find the number of cents each
  person has?

- How can the four friends share their money
  so that everyone can buy a ticket to the show?

Are You Ready?

Complete these problems to review prior concepts and skills
you will need for this module.

Multiplication Facts

Find the product.

1 $4 \times 8 =$ _____

2 _____ $= 8 \times 8$

3 $9 \times 3 =$ _____

4 _____ $= 9 \times 10$

5 $7 \times 2 =$ _____

6 _____ $= 7 \times 6$

Add Whole Numbers

Estimate. Then find the sum.

7 $386 + 246 =$ _____

Estimate: _____

8 $35 + 346 =$ _____

Estimate: _____

9 $82 + 579 =$ _____

Estimate: _____

10 $463 + 96 =$ _____

Estimate: _____

Multiply with 3-Digit Numbers

Find the product.

11 $\begin{array}{r} 582 \\ \times\ 34 \\ \hline \end{array}$

12 $\begin{array}{r} 435 \\ \times\ 73 \\ \hline \end{array}$

13 $\begin{array}{r} 391 \\ \times\ 42 \\ \hline \end{array}$

14 $\begin{array}{r} 843 \\ \times\ 58 \\ \hline \end{array}$

15 $\begin{array}{r} 496 \\ \times\ 95 \\ \hline \end{array}$

16 $\begin{array}{r} 207 \\ \times\ 23 \\ \hline \end{array}$

Name _____

Represent Decimal Multiplication

(I Can) find the product of two decimals to
the tenths place by using a decimal model.

Spark Your Learning

Mr. Kasim has a collection of 100 coins from
around the world. Of the 100 coins, 0.7 are
in the shape of a circle. Of these circular
coins, 0.3 have holes. How many coins in his
collection are in the shape of a circle and
have holes?

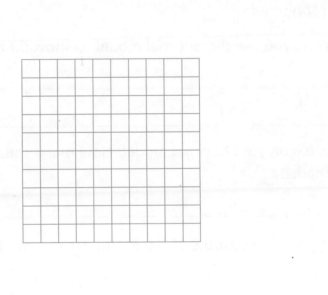

PAIRS

💬 **Turn and Talk** How can you tell whether the product of
0.7 and 0.3 is greater than or less than each factor?

Build Understanding

1 Mrs. Varga has a collection of postage stamps. Of her stamps, 0.6 are from a country outside of the United States. Of those stamps, 0.8 are from the last 5 years. What decimal represents the part of her collection that is from outside of the United States and from the last 5 years?

Use the decimal model.

A. What multiplication expression models the situation?

_____

B. Think about what each column of the decimal model represents.

- How can you use the decimal model to show 0.6?

_____

_____

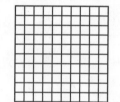

- Show 0.6 on your decimal model. How many squares are shaded?

_____

C. How do you represent 0.8 of 0.6 in the decimal model?

_____

D. How many squares are shaded to represent 0.8 × 0.6?

_____

E. What part of Mrs. Varga's collection is from outside of the United States and from the last 5 years?

_____

 Turn and Talk How can you use your decimal model for 0.8 × 0.6 to find the product 0.8 × 1.2?

2 Hakeem also collects postage stamps. One of his stamps shows an older model telephone. What is the area of the stamp?

0.9 in.

1.2 in.

A. What multiplication expression models the area?

_____

B. How can you represent 1.2 in the decimal model?

_____

_____

_____

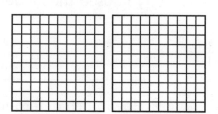

C. How many squares are shaded?

_____

D. How do you represent 0.9 of 1.2 in the decimal model?

_____

_____

E. What is the area of the stamp?

_____

• •

Check Understanding

1 Jason has a silver dollar that weighs 0.9 ounce. He has a nickel that weighs 0.2 of the weight of the silver dollar. How much does the nickel weigh? Use the decimal model.

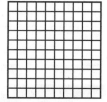

_____

2 Kali has a banner with a width of 0.3 meter and a length of 1.5 meters. What is the area of the banner? Use the decimal model.

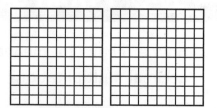

_____

On Your Own

3 (MP) **Model with Mathematics** Carter has a bottle of detergent that holds 1.8 liters. He fills a container that is 0.4 the size of the bottle. How much detergent is in the smaller container?

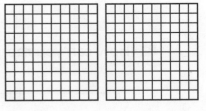

- Write a multiplication expression that models the situation. Use the decimal model. Then explain how you used the model.

_____

_____

- How much detergent is in the smaller container? _____

Find the area of the rectangle described. Use the decimal model.

4 length = 0.8 cm

width = 0.3 cm

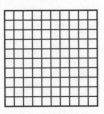

area = _____

5 length = 0.5 m

width = 1.3 m

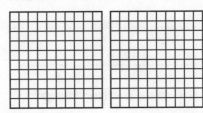

area = _____

6 **Open Ended** Write a word problem that can be represented by

the decimal model shown. _____

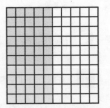

_____

_____

✦ I'm in a Learning Mindset!

How effective for me was it to use decimal models for understanding decimal multiplication?

_____

Name _____

Multiply Decimals

(I Can) multiply two decimal numbers by applying an understanding
of place value.

Spark Your Learning

Nikki buys items from the bulk bins at the grocery store. The table
shows the item, the number of pounds that Nikki buys, and the cost
for one pound of the item.

Sort each item by cost for the amount that Nikki buys.

Grocery Items		
Item	Weight (in pounds)	Cost for One Pound
Almonds	1.2	$5.89
Trail Mix	2.6	$4.42
White Rice	1.6	$0.89
Lentils	0.7	$0.83
Walnuts	1.8	$7.72
Red Beans	0.5	$1.29

Less Than $1	Between $1 and $10	Greater Than $10

SMALL GROUPS

Turn and Talk Which item(s) between $1 and $10 cost more
than $5? How do you know?

Build Understanding

1 Oliver is making a pasta salad. He needs 2.3 ounces of dry pasta for 1 serving. He wants to make 7.5 servings. How much dry pasta does he need?

A. What multiplication expression models the situation? _____

B. What is an estimate for the product? How did you find it?

_____

_____

C. How can finding the product 75 × 23 help you to find the product 7.5 × 2.3?

_____

_____

_____

D. What is the product 75 × 23?
23
× 75
———

E. How can you use your estimate to determine the placement of the decimal point in the whole-number product?

_____

_____

F. How much dry pasta does Oliver need? _____

 Turn and Talk If the amount for one serving increases from 2.3 ounces to 2.6 ounces, does that change the placement of the decimal point? Explain your answer.

Step It Out

2 ▸ Marta weighs some dry black beans. Her mother asks her to get 1.5 times as much. How many pounds of beans should Marta get?

2.36 lb

A. To find the product 1.5 × 2.36, first find 15 × 236.

$$\begin{array}{r} 236 \\ \times\ 15 \\ \hline \end{array}$$

B. Complete each equation.

236 × _____ = 2.36   15 × _____ = 1.5

C. By how many decimal place values does 236 differ from 2.36? _____

D. By how many decimal place values does 15 differ from 1.5? _____

E. The actual product differs from the whole-number product by the total number of decimal place values. By how many decimal place values does 15 × 236 differ from 1.5 × 2.36? _____

F. How many pounds of beans should Marta get? _____

Turn and Talk How can you use the result to find the product 0.15 × 23.6?

Check Understanding 〔Math Board〕

1 Max buys 4.6 pounds of apples that cost $3.40 for one pound.

• Write an equation to estimate the total cost. _____

• What is the total cost? _____

Multiply.

2
$$\begin{array}{r} 7.3 \\ \times\ 3.6 \\ \hline \end{array}$$

3
$$\begin{array}{r} 52.1 \\ \times\ 0.8 \\ \hline \end{array}$$

4
$$\begin{array}{r} 12.8 \\ \times\ 7.3 \\ \hline \end{array}$$

On Your Own

5 Mr. Yuen is buying carpeting for the conference room. He uses the floor plan to determine its area.

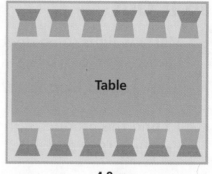

Table   3.25 m

4.8 m

• Write an equation to estimate the area of the conference room.

_____

• What is the product 48 × 325? _____

• What is the area of the conference room? Explain how you used your estimate to find the answer.

_____

_____

Multiply.

6   7.2
     × 1.3

7   4.79
     × 6.2

8   57.23
     × 3.4

9 **Art** Claude Monet painted *Water Lilies* between 1914 and 1926. This painting is in three panels and has its own wall in the Museum of Modern Art in New York City. How much wall space does the painting cover?

_____

2.1 meters

12.8 meters

✦ I'm in a Learning Mindset!

How was I able to explain my thinking about multiplying decimals?

_____

Name

Multiply Decimals with Zeros in the Product

(**I Can**) write the correct number of zeros in the product
of two decimal numbers.

Step It Out

1 ▶ Jamal and his friends arrive at
the train station. The map shows
distances to various attractions
from the station. His guidebook
recommends a sandwich shop 0.2 of
the way from the train station to the
zoo. How far is the sandwich shop
from the train station?

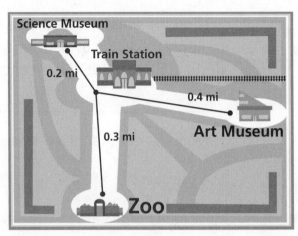

Science Museum
Train Station
0.2 mi
0.4 mi
0.3 mi
Art Museum
Zoo

A. To solve the problem, find the product 0.2 × 0.3. What is the
related whole-number product?

_____

B. How many decimal place values are needed in the
decimal product?

_____

C. There is only one digit in the whole-number product. Write
zeros, as needed, to the left of the whole-number product
so that there are enough digits to place the decimal point
correctly. What is the decimal product?

_____

D. How far is the sandwich shop from the train station?

_____

Turn and Talk Do you need to write zeros to the left
of the whole-number product if the decimal product is
0.4 × 0.3? Explain.

Step It Out

2 The animals at a zoo are exhibited in rectangular-shaped spaces. What is the area of the giraffe space? What is the area of the zebra space?

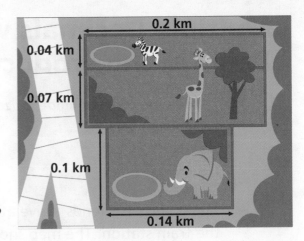

A. To find the area of the giraffe space, multiply 0.2 and 0.07. How many decimal place values are in each factor?

_____

B. How many decimal place values are in

the product 0.2 × 0.07? _____

C. How many digits are in the whole-number product 2 × 7?

_____

D. How many zeros do you need to write to the left of the whole-number product 2 × 7 to place the decimal point in the product 0.2 × 0.07?

_____

E. What is the area of the giraffe space? _____

F. Find the area of the zebra space. Multiply 0.2 and 0.04. How many decimal place values are in the product 0.2 × 0.04?

_____

G. How many zeros do you need to write to the left of the whole-number product 2 × 4 to place the decimal point in the product 0.2 × 0.04?

_____

H. What is the area of the zebra space? _____

 Turn and Talk Is the area of the elephant space equal to either of the other two animal spaces? How can you tell?

© Houghton Mifflin Harcourt Publishing Company

410

Check Understanding 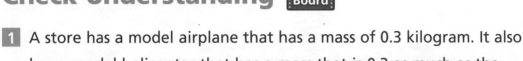 Math Board

1 A store has a model airplane that has a mass of 0.3 kilogram. It also has a model helicopter that has a mass that is 0.3 as much as the mass of the airplane. What is the mass of the helicopter?

_____

Multiply.

2	0.6	**3**	0.03	**4**	0.08
	× 0.1		× 0.3		× 0.4

On Your Own

5 The reptile and amphibian exhibit has a tree frog that is 0.4 as long as the bullfrog shown. What is the length of the tree frog? Explain how you know.

0.2 m

_____

_____

_____

6 Sweet potatoes cost $0.85 for one pound. If Jaylen buys

0.8 pound of sweet potatoes, how much does he pay? _____

Multiply.

7	0.1	**8**	0.3	**9**	0.8
	× 0.7		× 0.4		× 0.5

10	0.06	**11**	0.02	**12**	0.09
	× 0.9		× 0.3		× 0.7

On Your Own

Multiply.

13 $0.8
    $\times$ 0.1

14 $0.05
    $\times$ 0.4

15 $0.60
    $\times$ 0.4

Find the unknown number.

16 ■ $\times$ 0.05 = 0.04   **17** 0.6 $\times$ ■ = 0.048   **18** 0.012 = 0.04 $\times$ ■

_____   _____   _____

19 Patricia has 0.3 liter of lemon juice. She needs 0.2 times as much as that amount for a recipe. How much lemon juice does she

need for the recipe? _____

20 (MP) **Construct Arguments** Geno multiplies 0.35 by 0.2 and gets 0.007. Elena says the product is 0.07. Who is correct? Explain how you know.

_____

_____

_____

21 (MP) **Attend to Precision** Which product is greater, 0.3 $\times$ 0.08 or 0.06 $\times$ 0.4? Explain how you know.

_____

_____

_____

22 (MP) **Reason** Explain how you know if the product of a decimal less than 1 to the tenths place and a decimal less than 1 to the hundredths place has zeros between the decimal point and the first nonzero digit to the right of the decimal point.

_____

_____

Concepts and Skills

1 Compare the products 2.35 × 0.8 and 235 × 8. By how many decimal places do the products differ?

_____

2 Select all the expressions that have a value of 0.024.

(A) 0.2 × 0.12   (D) 0.3 × 0.8

(B) 1.2 × 0.2   (E) 0.8 × 0.03

(C) 0.04 × 0.6

3 What is the value of 0.7 × 0.6? Use the decimal model.

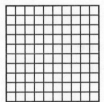

4 (MP) **Use Tools** Which is the area of the rectangle? Tell what strategy or tool you will use to answer the question, explain your choice, and then find the answer.

7.5 cm

4.3 cm

(A) 3.225 sq cm   (C) 322.5 sq cm

(B) 32.25 sq cm   (D) 3,225 sq cm

_____

_____

5 Which is the unknown value?

$0.8 \times \blacksquare = 0.056$

- (A) 0.007
- (B) 0.07
- (C) 0.7
- (D) 7

6 The cost for 1 pound of onions is $0.80. Cheyenne buys 3.4 pounds of onions. How much does she pay?

_____

7 What is the value of 0.4×1.6? Use the decimal model.

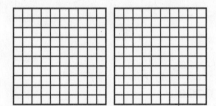

_____

8 The Highland Park Trail is 6.38 kilometers long. Ashley starts at the beginning of the trail and hikes 0.7 of the trail to see a waterfall. How far along the trail is the waterfall?

- (A) 44.66 kilometers
- (B) 42.66 kilometers
- (C) 4.466 kilometers
- (D) 4.266 kilometers

9 What is the value of 2.4×7.96?

_____

10 Select all the expressions that have a value of 0.096.

- (A) 0.1×9.6
- (B) 0.1×0.96
- (C) 0.3×0.32
- (D) 0.16×0.6
- (E) 0.8×1.2

Divide Decimals and Convert Metric Units

Sales Assistant

If you want a career in sales, a job as a sales assistant is a great place to start. The role of the sales assistant varies from job to job. It could involve preparing items to be sold, talking to customers, or restocking shelves. Many people use a job as a sales assistant as a starting point to later become sales managers, regional managers, and sales directors.

People who work in sales need skills such as relationship-building and being able to communicate well, both by speaking and by writing. They have to be able to explain how the products being sold are good choices and how they fill a need.

Did you know that some sales people get commissions, or extra money, for meeting a goal of selling a certain number of their product?

STEM Task:

Think of an improvement for an existing product. Before the invention of the paper clip, people used pins to hold papers together. The paper clip is more efficient and safer than a pin. Is there something you would like to improve? For example, is there something you could change on a backpack or a bike helmet to make it better? Draw a picture of your product and explain the improved features to try to "sell" it to a classmate.

Learning Mindset
Challenge-Seeking Sets Achievable Stretch Goals

Setting goals for yourself is important, and it is the first step to achieving them. When you set a goal, remember that the amount of time or the effort it takes to achieve goals is not the same for everyone. If there is something you would like to do, do not be discouraged if it is difficult at first. For example, you might want to join a choir but feel you do not sing well right now. But if you practice, you can learn to sing better. Just remember that you do not have to achieve your goal all at once. Set smaller milestone goals along the way to a bigger goal.

Reflect

Q Did you have a goal to fulfill a need with your product? Describe the need it fulfills.

Q Were you able to convince your classmate that your product is a good idea? If not, what else could you change to improve the product?

Divide Decimals

WHAT CAN I BUY?

Lorna has $5 to spend at the grocery store. She wants to buy 2 items and has a coupon for $1 off any purchase of $5 or more.

- What are the two most expensive items that Lorna can

  buy using her coupon? _____

Bag of Rice
$2.45

Broccoli
$1.75

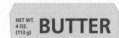

Butter
$2.80

Hummus
$3.39

Milk
$3.59

 Turn and Talk

- Explain how to solve the problem. How much of her $5 does Lorna spend?

- Suppose Lorna uses her money and the coupon to purchase 3 items. If she can buy 2 or more of one item, is it possible for her to spend a greater amount? Explain.

Are You Ready?

Complete these problems to review prior concepts and skills you will need for this module.

Division Facts

Find the quotient.

1 18 ÷ 2 = _____

2 3)‾21‾

3 32 ÷ 8 = _____

4 6)‾30‾

5 56 ÷ 7 = _____

6 9)‾27‾

Equivalent Decimals

Write the equivalent decimal in hundredths.

7 5.6

8 3.9

9 12.2

_____   _____   _____

Write the equivalent decimal in tenths.

10 8.40

11 6.20

12 0.80

_____   _____   _____

Division

Find the quotient.

13 23)‾552‾

14 38)‾3,990‾

15 42)‾1,478‾

16 32)‾7,884‾

17 64)‾1,408‾

18 16)‾2,211‾

Name

Understand Decimal Division Patterns

(I Can) use patterns to place the decimal point in a quotient.

Spark Your Learning

Jada is playing a sorting game with a deck of math cards.
Each card has an expression on one side. She lays out 10 of the cards.

$752 \div 100$	$936 \div 1{,}000$	0.842×10^2	$842 \div 10$	0.936×10
$93.6 \div 10^2$	$84.2 \div 10^2$	$7{,}520 \div 10^2$	0.752×10^3	$842 \div 10^3$

Sort the expressions on the cards in the boxes.

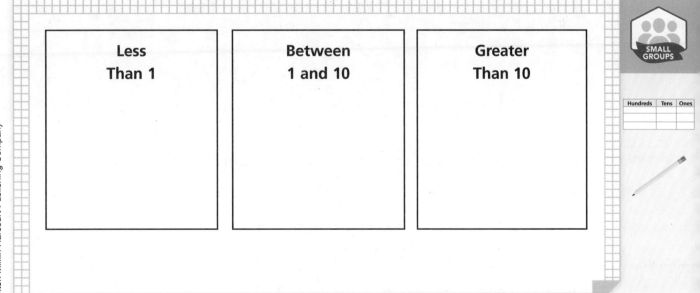

Less Than 1	Between 1 and 10	Greater Than 10

SMALL GROUPS

Hundreds	Tens	Ones

Turn and Talk How can you use place value to determine the value of the 7 in the quotient $752 \div 100$?

Build Understanding

1 The factory making the math cards ships a box with decks of cards to a warehouse. How much does each deck of cards weigh?

1,000 decks

Net weight: 275 pounds

A. How can you determine the weight of one deck of cards? _____

B. Dividing by 1,000 is the same as multiplying by what fraction? _____

C. What is the decimal equivalent of $\frac{1}{1,000}$? _____

D. Complete the pattern.

$275 \times 1 =$ _____

$275 \times 0.1 =$ _____

$275 \times 0.01 =$ _____

$275 \times 0.001 =$ _____

E. Write a pattern for dividing 275 by 1, 10, 100, and 1,000.

F. What can you conclude about the relationship between the patterns in parts D and E?

_____

_____

G. How much does each deck of cards weigh? _____

 Turn and Talk How does the position of the decimal point change as you divide by increasing powers of 10?

2 A store receives and sells 1,000 decks of the math cards. If the amount received from selling 1,000 decks of cards is $9,450, what is the price for each deck of cards?

A. How will you find the price for each deck of cards?

_____

B. Divide 9,450 by 1, 10, 100, and 1,000

- using numerical form.   • using exponential form.

C. How is the change in the position of the decimal point related to the exponent for the power of 10?

_____

_____

D. How do the place values of the digits in the quotients in your pattern change as you divide by increasing powers of 10?

_____

_____

E. To find the cost for each deck of cards, how will the decimal point shift?

_____

F. What is the price for each deck of cards? _____

Turn and Talk How is the pattern of multiplying by 1, 0.1, 0.01, and 0.001 related to the pattern of dividing by 10^0, 10^1, 10^2, and 10^3?

Build Understanding

3 The factory making the math cards also produces game
tokens. They sell them in packages of 100 tokens. Each
package weighs 28 ounces. How much do 1,000 packages
weigh? How much does one game token weigh?

A. What expression using a power of 10 describes the
weight of 1,000 packages?

_____

B. How much do 1,000 packages weigh? How do you know?

_____

_____

_____

C. What expression using a power of 10 describes the weight of
1 game token?

_____

D. How much does 1 game token weigh? How do you know?

_____

_____

 Turn and Talk How do you find $537 \div 10^3$?

Check Understanding

1 A shipment of 1,000 toy cars weighs
538 pounds. How many pounds does
1 toy car weigh? Find the answer
by using a pattern with powers of 10.

_____

© Houghton Mifflin Harcourt Publishing Company

On Your Own

2 The container holds 100 servings of juice.

6.6 gal

- Show a pattern to find the amount of juice in one serving.

- How many gallons are there in one serving?

  _____

Complete the pattern.

3 278 ÷ 1 = _____

278 ÷ 10 = _____

278 ÷ 100 = _____

4 $73.6 \div 10^0$ = _____

$73.6 \div 10^1$ = _____

$73.6 \div 10^2$ = _____

5 6.5 ÷ 1 = _____

6.5 ÷ 10 = _____

6.5 ÷ 100 = _____

6 934 ÷ 1 = _____

934 ÷ 10 = _____

934 ÷ 100 = _____

934 ÷ 1,000 = _____

7 $590 \div 10^0$ = _____

$590 \div 10^1$ = _____

$590 \div 10^2$ = _____

$590 \div 10^3$ = _____

8 $81 \div 10^0$ = _____

$81 \div 10^1$ = _____

$81 \div 10^2$ = _____

$81 \div 10^3$ = _____

9 (MP) **Use Structure** Explain how to divide 47 by 10^3.

_____

_____

_____

On Your Own

Use the table for 10–13.

Ingredients for 1,000 Servings of Pasta Sauce	
Ingredient	**Amount**
Crushed tomatoes	1,750 ounces
Tomato sauce	750 ounces
Sausage	60 pounds
Ground beef	45 pounds
Italian seasoning	5 cups
Onions	64 cups

10 How many ounces of crushed tomatoes are in one serving?

_____

11 How many more pounds of sausage than ground beef are in one serving?

_____

12 How many cups of Italian seasoning are needed for 10 servings?

_____

13 How many cups of onions are needed for 100 servings? _____

Find the unknown number.

14 $593 \div \blacksquare = 5.93$

_____

15 $\blacksquare \div 1,000 = 3.64$

_____

16 $0.468 = 468 \div \blacksquare$

_____

17 $\blacksquare \div 10^2 = 8.17$

_____

18 $0.076 = 76 \div \blacksquare$

_____

19 $64.1 = \blacksquare \div 10^3$

_____

20 (MP) **Use Structure** Describe how you can use a place-value chart to help you divide a number by a power of 10.

_____

_____

 I'm in a Learning Mindset!

What would I like to learn more about when I'm studying division patterns?

_____

Name

Represent Division of Decimals by Whole Numbers

(I Can) use a concrete or visual model to divide a decimal by a whole number.

Spark Your Learning

Nicole and her five friends can buy bottles of lemonade individually, or they can buy a six-pack together. How much does each person save on the price of a bottle of lemonade if they buy the six-pack? Justify your answer.

one bottle $1.00

6-pack $4.80

Turn and Talk Nicole and her five friends buy a large bag of popcorn to share for $8.40. How much does each person pay?

Build Understanding

1 Yolanda buys trail mix from the bulk bin and divides the
trail mix evenly among herself and three friends. How many
pounds of trail mix does each person get?

**Use base-ten blocks to show how much each person gets.
Remember that a flat represents one, a long represents
one tenth, and a small cube represents one hundredth.**

5.6 lb

A. How did you use base-ten blocks to represent 5.6?

_____

B. Describe how you divided 5.6 into 4 equal groups.

_____

_____

_____

C. What number is represented by each group? How do you know?

_____

D. How many pounds of trail mix does each person get? _____

 Turn and Talk If Yolanda adds another pound of trail mix, how
does the amount each person gets change? Explain how you know.

© Houghton Mifflin Harcourt Publishing Company

2 Paul buys a package of 8 bouncy balls. How much does each ball weigh?

BOUNCY BALLS
8 Balls
Net Wt: 7.36 oz

Use a quick picture to show how much each ball weighs.

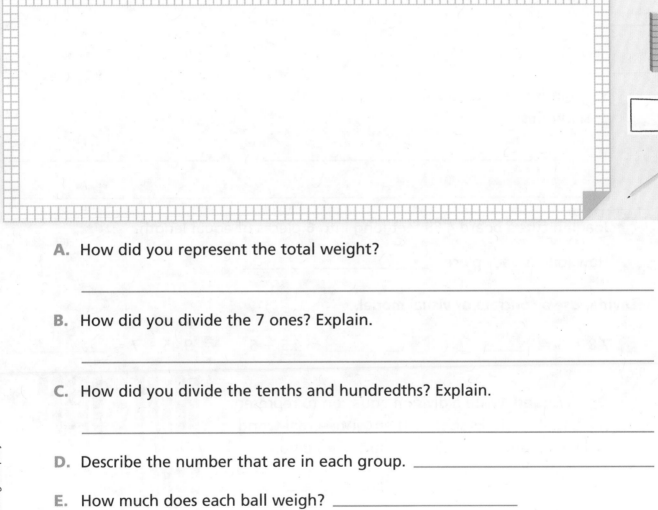

A. How did you represent the total weight?

_____

B. How did you divide the 7 ones? Explain.

_____

C. How did you divide the tenths and hundredths? Explain.

_____

D. Describe the number that are in each group. _____

E. How much does each ball weigh? _____

· ·

Check Understanding `Math Board`

Solve using a concrete or visual model.

1 Carson divides 4.2 pounds of nuts into 6 equal servings. How much does each serving weigh?

_____

2 Tasha buys 6 avocados for $7.14 at the store. How much does each avocado cost?

_____

On Your Own

3 **(MP)** **Use Tools** A race official wants to place water stations between the start and finish lines so that the race course is divided into 3 equal sections. What is the distance from the start of the race to the first water station?

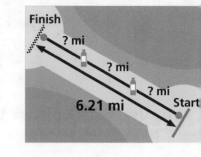

- Draw to represent the problem.

- What is the distance? Explain how you used your drawing to show this.

_____

_____

4 Joaquin cuts a board 4.68 feet long into 6 pieces of equal length.

How long is each piece? _____

Divide. Use a concrete or visual model.

5 7.8 ÷ 6 = _____   **6** _____ = 4.5 ÷ 5   **7** 9.45 ÷ 7 = _____

8 **Open Ended** Write a division equation to represent the base-ten blocks shown. Then write a real-world problem that can be solved using the equation.

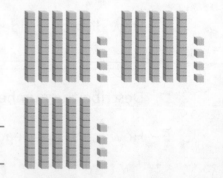

_____

_____

🔲 I'm in a Learning Mindset!

What evidence do I have that I have correctly divided a decimal by a whole number?

_____

Name _____

Assess Reasonableness of Quotients

(I Can) estimate the quotient of a decimal division problem by using compatible numbers.

Spark Your Learning

A food store received a shipment of the spice turmeric. The store manager is trying to decide whether to sell the turmeric in 3 equal bags, 4 equal bags, 5 equal bags, or 6 equal bags. She wants the turmeric in each bag to weigh between 0.3 pound and 0.4 pound. Into how many bags should she separate the turmeric?

Turmeric

2.3 lb

SMALL GROUPS

Turn and Talk Will the weight of the turmeric in each bag be closer to 0.3 pound or 0.4 pound? Explain.

Build Understanding

Saffron
1.9 oz

1 A cook bought an envelope of the spice saffron. She wants to store equal amounts of the saffron in 8 glass jars. About how much saffron will the cook put in each jar?

A. What is an expression you could use to model the problem?

_____

B. A compatible number is close to the dividend and can be divided evenly by the divisor. How can you use a compatible number to make your estimate?

_____

_____

C. Do you think that your estimate is more than or less than the actual amount of saffron that will be put into each jar? Why?

_____

_____

D. What is a different compatible number that you could have used to estimate? What is the estimate?

_____

E. Is this estimate more than or less than the actual amount? How do you know?

_____

_____

F. The cook thinks that there will be about 0.23 oz of saffron in each jar. Is this amount reasonable? Explain.

_____

_____

 Turn and Talk Would 0.28 ounce be a more reasonable estimate than 0.23 ounce? Explain.

Step It Out

2 ▸ Twenty-three friends decide to order some food. The friends decide to share the total cost evenly. About how much will each friend pay for the food?

MARCO'S PIZZERIA

Pizza
Drinks
Salad

Total: $148.80

_____

A. Write a division expression for the problem.

_____

B. Estimate the quotient. To make numbers compatible, you may have to adjust both the divisor and the dividend.

- To what number could you adjust the divisor? _____

- To what number could you adjust the dividend so that it can be divided evenly by your adjusted divisor? _____

C. What is your estimate? _____

D. About how much will each friend pay for the food? _____

 Turn and Talk When do you not adjust the divisor to make numbers compatible?

• •

Check Understanding [Math Board]

1 A ribbon is 0.42 meter long. Sean cuts the ribbon into 9 equal pieces. Is 0.05 meter a reasonable estimate for the length of each piece of ribbon? Explain.

_____

_____

_____

Estimate the quotient by using compatible numbers.

2 158.2 ÷ 7 Dividend: _____ Divisor: _____ Quotient: _____

3 183.75 ÷ 18 Dividend: _____ Divisor: _____ Quotient: _____

On Your Own

4 (MP) **Model with Mathematics** Kathy pours equal amounts of the water from the bucket into each of 7 bottles. About how much water goes into each bottle?

6.5 liters

- Write a division expression for the problem. _____

- Rename the dividend as a number of tenths, and adjust it to be a compatible number with 7.

  _____

- Estimate the quotient. About how much water goes into each bottle?

  _____

5 Terence collects 0.61 pound of sand along a river. He wants to distribute the sand equally among 8 buckets. Is it reasonable for Terence to put 0.08 pound of sand in each bucket? Explain.

_____

_____

6 **Financial Literacy** Ms. Smythe buys a bike on credit for $434.95. To avoid paying interest, she agrees to make 12 equal monthly payments for the bike. About how much will

Ms. Smythe pay each month? _____

Estimate the quotient by using compatible numbers.

7 21.8 ÷ 6 Dividend: _____ Divisor: _____ Quotient: _____

8 141.19 ÷ 32 Dividend: _____ Divisor: _____ Quotient: _____

 I'm in a Learning Mindset!

What types of decisions did I make when estimating decimal quotients?

_____

Name _____

Divide Decimals by Whole Numbers

(I Can) divide a decimal by a whole number.

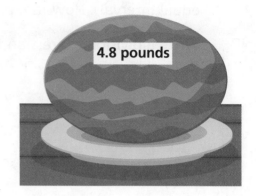

4.8 pounds

Spark Your Learning

Mr. Lewis bought a watermelon for a summer picnic. At home, he carves the watermelon and makes 12 bowls of watermelon pieces. Each bowl weighs the same amount. How much does each bowl weigh?

SMALL GROUPS

 Turn and Talk How would your solution change if the watermelon weighed 48 pounds?

Build Understanding

1 Janet builds a ladder to a tree fort. She places the steps at equal intervals. How far apart are the steps?

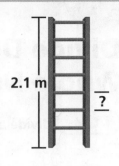

2.1 m

Write a division expression to represent the situation. Draw to show the division.

A. How did you represent 2.1?

_____

B. Are you asked to find an estimate or an exact answer? How do you know?

_____

_____

C. Describe how you were able to solve the problem.

_____

_____

_____

D. How much does each group represent? _____

E. How far apart are the steps of the ladder? _____

 Turn and Talk How is using base-ten blocks to find the quotient similar to using place value?

Step It Out

2 A scientist collects a sand sample from the shore of a beach. He stores equal amounts of the sand in each of 38 containers. How much sand does the scientist put in each container?

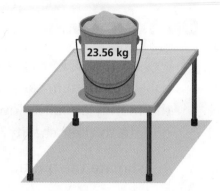
23.56 kg

A. Write an expression to model the situation.

_____

B. Use compatible numbers to estimate. Show your work.

_____

_____

C. To find the actual quotient, divide the numbers as you would if there were no decimal point.

D. Use your estimate to place the decimal point in the quotient. Write a zero to show there are no ones. Write the quotient.

E. How much sand does the scientist put in each container?

_____

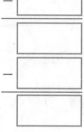
$3\,8\overline{)2\,3\,.\,5\,6}$

 Turn and Talk How can you use inverse operations to check your answer?

- -

Check Understanding Math Board

1 Halley has 3.2 liters of lemonade. She pours equal amounts of the lemonade into 8 cups. How much lemonade does Halley pour into each cup?

_____

Estimate the quotient. Then find the actual quotient.

2 $51\overline{)47.43}$

3 $87\overline{)20.01}$

_____

On Your Own

4 (MP) **Attend to Precision** For a charity drive, 12 students collect aluminum cans to sell to a recycler. They agree to share the money equally. How much money does each student get to donate to their charity?

$82.44

- Estimate the quotient. Show your work.

_____

- To find the actual quotient, divide the numbers as you would if there were no decimal point. Then place the decimal point in the quotient.

- How much money will each student get to donate?

_____

Divide.

5 6)27.6

6 3)72.9

7 8)17.28

8 42)331.8

9 23)239.2

10 34)208.42

 **I'm in a Learning Mindset!**

When I divide a decimal by a whole number, how do I break the problem into smaller steps?

_____

_____

© Houghton Mifflin Harcourt Publishing Company

Name _____

Represent Decimal Division

(I Can) divide a decimal by a decimal using a concrete or
visual model.

Spark Your Learning

A mouse finds a bag of sunflower seeds. The mouse
eats 0.2 ounce of sunflower seeds each day. How many
days does the bag of sunflower seeds last?

SMALL GROUPS

 Turn and Talk How can you check your answer?

© Houghton Mifflin Harcourt Publishing Company

Build Understanding

1 A scientist has a container of ocean water. She pours 0.6 liter of water into each of several jars. How many jars does the scientist need?

Ocean Water 1.8 liters

Write the expression to represent the situation. Use decimal models to show the division.

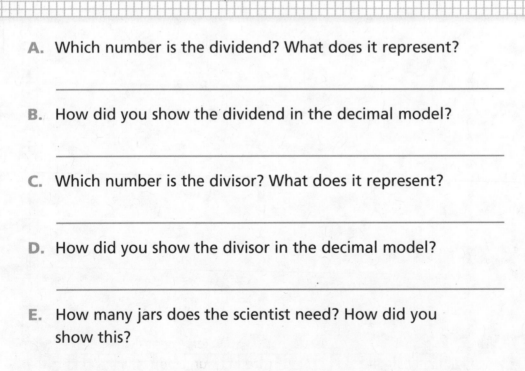

A. Which number is the dividend? What does it represent?

_____

B. How did you show the dividend in the decimal model?

_____

C. Which number is the divisor? What does it represent?

_____

D. How did you show the divisor in the decimal model?

_____

E. How many jars does the scientist need? How did you show this?

_____

 Turn and Talk How will the answer change if the scientist pours 0.2 liter of water into each jar? Explain.

2 A scientist needs 0.28 square meter of gold foil to make one satellite antenna. How many antennas can she make with the foil?

1.12 square meters

Write the expression to represent the situation. Use decimal models to show the division.

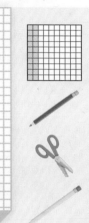

A. Which number is the dividend? What does it represent?

_____

B. How did you show the dividend?

_____

C. Which number is the divisor? What does it represent?

_____

D. How did you show the divisor?

_____

E. How many antennas can the scientist make? How did you show this?

_____

 Turn and Talk How can you check that your decimal model is correct?

Step It Out

3 Esperanza makes 2 quarts of soup. How many bowls can she fill with soup?

A. Write an expression to represent the situation.

_____

0.4 quart

B. Use decimal models to find the quotient.

C. How does your decimal model show the quotient?

_____

D. How many bowls can Esperanza fill with soup? _____

 Turn and Talk How could you use hundredths models to solve the problem?

Check Understanding

Draw a picture to represent the situation. Identify the dividend and divisor. Then solve.

1 Julio walks 2.4 miles from his home to the park. He stops to look for birds every 0.3 mile. How many times does Julio stop?

Dividend: _____

Divisor: _____

_____

On Your Own

2 **(MP)** **Use Tools** Anya takes $1.75 to the store. How many pears can she buy?

- Write an expression to represent the situation.

  _____

- Use decimal models to find the quotient.

- How many pears can Anya buy? _____

Use a concrete or visual model. Identify the dividend and divisor in the problem. Then solve.

3 A sack contains 4.2 pounds of sand. Stan wants to put 0.6 pound of sand in each flowerpot. How many flowerpots can he fill?

Dividend: _____

Divisor: _____

_____

4 Candice needs 0.8 pint of milk to make a batch of butter. How many batches can she make with 2.4 pints of milk?

Dividend: _____

Divisor: _____

_____

5 A bird hops 0.72 meter. If each hop it takes is 0.09 meter, how many hops does the bird take?

Dividend: _____

Divisor: _____

_____

6 A sticker costs $0.64. Ronald spends $3.84 on stickers. How many stickers does Ronald buy?

Dividend: _____

Divisor: _____

_____

On Your Own

7 **(MP)** **Use Tools** Diana has a board. She wants to cut the board into equal pieces 0.7 meter long. How many pieces can she cut from the board?

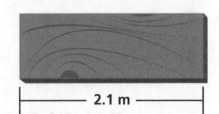

|— 2.1 m —|

- Draw a decimal model to find the answer.

- How many pieces can she cut from the board?

_____

Use decimal models to find the quotient.

8 0.8 ÷ 0.2 _____

9 1 ÷ 0.2 _____

10 0.56 ÷ 0.14 _____

11 1.47 ÷ 0.49 _____

12 **Open Ended** Write and solve a word problem for the division shown by the decimal model.

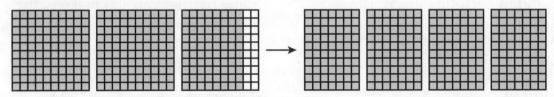

_____

_____

 I'm in a Learning Mindset!

What parts of dividing a decimal by a decimal am I comfortable doing on my own?

_____

Name _____

Divide Decimals

(I Can) divide a decimal by a decimal.

Step It Out

1 ▷ Marisol sets up a lemonade stand. At the end of the day, she has made $8.75. How many cups of lemonade did Marisol sell?

A. What is the division problem you are trying to solve?

_____

B. How could you write this problem as a fraction?

_____

C. What number could you multiply the numerator and denominator by to write an equivalent fraction with whole numbers? What is the equivalent fraction?

_____

D. Write and solve the new division problem shown by the equivalent fraction.

_____

E. How can you use this quotient to solve the original division problem?

_____

_____

F. How many cups of lemonade did Marisol sell? _____

Turn and Talk To make division easier to understand and to carry out, which number do you think is more important to be a whole number, the divisor or the dividend? Explain.

Step It Out

2 ▸ James rides his bike 16.32 miles. He rides about 9.6 miles each hour. How many hours does it take James to ride this distance?

A. What division expression models the situation?

_____

B. Estimate the answer. Show your work.

_____

C. How can you write the division problem as a fraction?

_____

D. Write an equivalent fraction with a whole-number denominator. How did you do this?

_____

_____

E. Write and solve the new division problem.

_____

F. How do you know that the quotient of the new division problem is the same as the quotient of the original division problem?

_____

_____

G. Is your answer reasonable? Explain.

_____

_____

H. How many hours does James ride? _____

 Turn and Talk Will you get the same answer if you multiply the dividend and divisor by 100 instead of by 10? Why is multiplying by 10 more efficient? Explain.

Check Understanding

1 A school shirt sells for $8.25. So far, $57.75 has been raised from selling the shirts. How many shirts have been sold?

_____

Divide.

2 12.76 ÷ 3.19

3 69.72 ÷ 4.2

4 93.5 ÷ 4.25

On Your Own

5 A peacock's display is 86.25 inches wide. The width of each of its feathers is 1.25 inches. How many feathers wide is the peacock's display?

_____

6 (MP) **Attend to Precision** Carlos sells coupon booklets for $5.50 apiece. He makes $60.50. Monica sells the same booklets for $4.75 each and makes $57. Who sells more booklets? How many more?

_____

Divide.

7 16.66 ÷ 3.4

8 192.5 ÷ 5.5

9 452.64 ÷ 24.6

10 343.2 ÷ 13.2

11 57.27 ÷ 8.3

12 391.84 ÷ 31.6

On Your Own

13 Alexa spends $37.74 buying toy train cars for her nieces. How many train cars does Alexa buy?

$6.29

_____

14 Shaniqua uses the ingredients shown in the table to make lemonade. She pours herself a 0.5-cup serving of the lemonade to sample the taste. She then pours the remaining lemonade into 0.75-cup glasses for her friends.

Ingredient	Amount
Water	5.5 cups
Lemon juice	2.5 cups

- Write an expression to model this situation.

_____

- How many glasses can Shaniqua fill? _____

15 (MP) **Model with Mathematics** Each mint in a roll has a thickness of 0.25 inch.

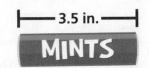

├── 3.5 in. ──┤

MINTS

- Write and solve an equation for how many mints are in the roll.

_____

- Describe how you solved the problem.

_____

_____

16 **Open Ended** Write and solve a word problem that uses the fraction $\frac{74.2}{5.3}$.

_____

_____

_____

Name _____

Write Zeros in the Dividend

(**I Can**) find a quotient by writing a zero in the dividend.

Step It Out

1 Charlie weighs 4 cantaloupe melons. They each weigh the same amount. How much does each cantaloupe weigh?

176.6 oz

A. Write a division expression to model the situation.

_____

B. Estimate the quotient.

_____

C. Divide 176.6 by 4.

- Write the decimal point in the quotient above the decimal point in the dividend.

- Divide the tens, ones, and tenths.

- Since the remainder is not 0, you need to continue dividing. Write a 0 in the hundredths place of the dividend. Regroup the leftover tenths as hundredths, so there are 20 hundredths. Now you can finish the division.

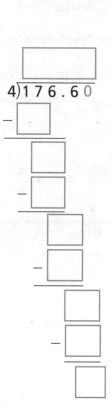

4)176.60

D. How much does each cantaloupe weigh?

_____

 Turn and Talk In the problem just completed, why is it acceptable to write 0 in the hundredths place?

Step It Out

2 ▸ Kelly wants to buy 78 ounces of almonds. Each bag can hold 31.2 ounces. How many bags of almonds does Kelly buy?

A. Write the division problem. _____

B. Rewrite the division so that the divisor is a whole number. Explain how you can do this.

_____

_____

C. Use long division to divide.

- Write the numbers in the long division.

- Divide the ones.

- Write a decimal point and a zero at the end of the dividend and then continue dividing.

D. How many bags of almonds does Kelly buy?

_____

 Turn and Talk What would you do if, after writing a decimal point and a 0 at the end of the dividend, your long division still had a non-zero remainder?

Check Understanding

1 A wood plank measures 92.4 inches long. It is cut into

5 equal pieces. How long is each piece? _____

Divide.

2 27.78 ÷ 0.5

3 318 ÷ 3.75

4 35.1 ÷ 0.6

On Your Own

5 Aubrey buys some apples that weigh 0.2 pound each. She cuts the apples and puts some of the halves on a scale. The total weight is shown on the scale. How many apples are on the scale?

_____

6 (MP) **Critique Reasoning** Zulu claims 27.5 divided by 0.2 is 13.75. Is she correct? Explain.

_____

_____

Divide.

7 21 ÷ 5

8 2.79 ÷ 0.18

9 10.4 ÷ 1.6

10 Use the table to answer the questions.

Item	Price
Jump rope	$2.29
Box of chalk	■
Flying disc	$1.50

• Lucinda buys a number of jump ropes. The total is $11.45. How many jump ropes does she buy?

_____

• Lucinda buys 8 boxes of chalk. The total is $14. How much does one box of chalk cost?

_____

• Lucinda buys 2 jump ropes and several flying discs. The total is $18.08. How many flying discs does she buy?

_____

On Your Own

11 (MP) **Model with Mathematics** Zachary has a container of worms for fishing. When empty, the mass of the container is 225 grams. With the worms in it, the container has a total mass of 751.4 grams. Each worm has a mass of 11.2 grams. How many worms are in the container? Write and solve an equation to model this situation.

12 A bathtub holds 112.7 gallons of water.

- How many 2.8-gallon buckets of water will it take to fill the bathtub?

- The bathtub is half full. How many 2.5-gallon buckets does it take to finish filling the tub?

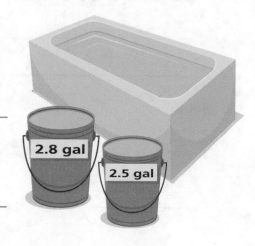

Divide.

13 $5\overline{)46.8}$

14 $2.3\overline{)13.57}$

15 $0.15\overline{)2.64}$

16 (MP) **Attend to Precision** A 6-pound bag of flour is used to make 8 equal batches of bread. How many pounds of flour go into each batch? How many zeros do you write in the dividend to solve the problem?

17 (MP) **Use Tools** Place points on the number line to show 4 equal lengths from 0 to 1.8. How long is each length?

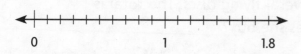

Review

42.5 ounces

Concepts and Skills

1 The honey in the jar was made in 23 beehives. Find an estimate for the amount of honey made in 1 beehive.

_____

2 **(MP) Use Tools** Divide. Tell what strategy or tool you will use to answer the question, explain your choice, and then find the answer.

$$14\overline{)49.98}$$

_____

3 Which group of base-ten blocks shows the correct quotient for $4.28 \div 4$?

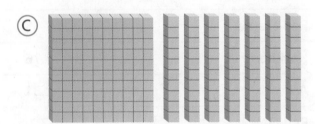

4 Write the decimal equation shown by the decimal model.

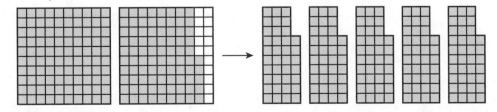

5 Into how many 31.5-inch pieces of firewood can the log be cut? _____

15.75 ft

6 What is value of the expression $837 \div 10^3$?

(A) 0.837

(C) 83,700

(B) 8.37

(D) 837,000

7 A jiffy is a measure of time. There are 100 jiffies in 1 second. How many seconds are there in 60 jiffies? Show your work.

_____

Use the table for 8–9. Each tree grows the same amount each year.

Type of Tree	Diameter Growth in 5.5 Years (in.)
Cottonwood	3.52
Red Maple	1.65
Hackberry	1.76
Ash	2.31
Red Oak	2.2

8 How much did the diameter of the cottonwood tree grow each year?

_____

9 Select all the trees that grew less than 0.4 inch in diameter each year.

(A) Cottonwood

(B) Red Maple

(C) Hackberry

(D) Ash

(E) Red Oak

18 Customary and Metric Measurement

How long is that distance?

- Write a unit of measurement from the box that matches the number below each picture. Units may be used more than once.

| centimeters |
| kilometers |
| meters |
| millimeters |

Distance from Earth to the moon

400,000 _____

Height of a door

2,000 _____

Height of a fire hydrant

80 _____

Length of an elephant

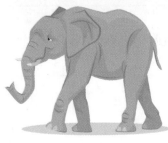

6,000 _____

 Turn and Talk

- How can you compare the measurements?

Are You Ready?

Complete these problems to review prior concepts and skills
you will need for this module.

Measure to the Nearest Centimeter

Use a centimeter ruler. Measure the length to the nearest centimeter.

1 _____ cm

2 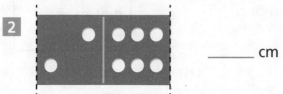 _____ cm

Choose Metric Units

Use benchmarks for length to choose the appropriate unit to measure each.
Write *centimeter*, *meter*, or *kilometer*.

3 height of your classroom

_____

4 distance across a state

_____

5 length of your shoe

_____

6 width of a schoolyard

_____

Choose Customary Units

Use benchmarks for length to choose the appropriate unit to measure each.
Write *inch*, *foot*, *yard*, or *mile*.

7 height of a bookcase

_____

8 distance from your home to
another state

_____

Name _____

Understand Metric Conversions

(I Can) convert between any two metric units
of length, liquid volume, or mass.

Step It Out

1 The Lesothosaurus was one of the smallest dinosaurs.
It had a mass of about 3,630 grams. About how many
kilograms was the mass of a Lesothosaurus?

You can use a conversion table to help you.

3,630 g = ▦ kg

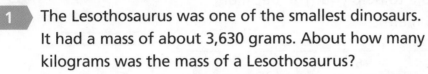

kilo- (k)	hecto- (h)	deka- (da)	meter (m) liter (L) gram (g)	deci- (d)	centi- (c)	milli- (m)

Factor of 10   Factor of 10   Factor of 10

A. Compare grams and kilograms.

- How many factors of 10 separate grams and kilograms?

_____

- How many grams are in one kilogram?

_____

B. To convert from grams to kilograms, are you converting from a
smaller unit to a larger unit or from a larger unit to a smaller unit?

_____

C. What operation will you use to make this conversion? _____

3,630 g ◯ _____ = _____

D. About how many kilograms was the mass of the Lesothosaurus?

_____

 Turn and Talk How would the conversion be different if you
were converting from kilograms to grams?

Step It Out

2 The largest wingspan for a dinosaur belonged to a species of *Quetzalcoatlus*. What was the wingspan in millimeters? What was the wingspan in kilometers?

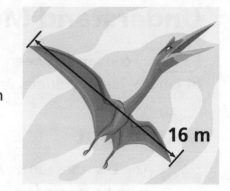

16 m

Use a conversion table to help you. The decimal point is shown in 16 meters.

kilo-	hecto-	deka-	meter liter gram	deci-	centi-	milli-
		1	6 .			

A. To convert the measure to millimeters, shift the decimal point to the location for a unit of millimeters. How many places and in which direction do you shift the decimal point?

_____

B. After shifting the decimal point, write zeros as needed to write the number of millimeters. What was the wingspan of the dinosaur?

_____

C. To convert the measure to kilometers, shift the decimal point to the location for a unit of kilometers. How many places and in which direction do you shift the decimal point?

_____

D. After shifting the decimal point, write zeros as needed to write the number of kilometers. What was the wingspan of the dinosaur?

_____

 Turn and Talk What mathematical operation can you use to convert a measure from meters to millimeters? From meters to kilometers? How do you know?

Check Understanding Math Board

1 The longest dinosaur, the *Argentinosaurus*, measured 40 meters long. How many centimeters long was the *Argentinosaurus*?

_____

Convert.

2 37 hL to L

3 261.9 cm to m

4 $9\frac{3}{4}$ g to mg

_____   _____   _____

On Your Own

5 **Social Studies** Archaeologists recently dug up what may be the world's oldest golden artifact in southern Bulgaria. This gold bead has a mass of 150 milligrams and measures 4 millimeters in diameter.

- How many grams is the mass of the bead? _____

- How many centimeters is its diameter? _____

6 (MP) **Model with Mathematics** Complete the equations to show how to convert 8.25 meters into the given unit of measure.

8.25 m × _____ = _____ dm

8.25 m × _____ = _____ cm

8.25 m × _____ = _____ mm

Convert.

7 4.6 m to cm

8 1.8 L to mL

9 58 g to kg

_____   _____   _____

10 6,257 cL to L

11 22.351 hg to mg

12 $84\frac{1}{2}$ km to m

_____   _____   _____

On Your Own

13 **STEM** There is a theory that the dinosaurs may have become extinct as a result of an asteroid crashing into Earth. The impact is believed to have left a crater in what is now the Yucatan Peninsula in Mexico. About how many meters wide is the crater?

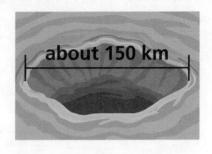

about 150 km

_____

14 (MP) **Reason** Are there less than 100,000, exactly 100,000, or greater than 100,000 milliliters in 1 kiloliter? Explain.

_____

_____

15 Two athletes are training for a long-distance race. Chris runs 2.75 kilometers 6 times each week. Kelly runs 1,250 meters 15 times each week. Whose training involves running a greater total distance each week? By how much more?

_____

16 The largest dinosaur eggs had a liquid volume of $3\frac{4}{5}$ liters. How many milliliters is this?

_____

17 (MP) **Attend to Precision** The average adult human body contains about 40 liters of fluid. If you want to give this amount as 40,000, what unit of measure do you use?

_____

18 (MP) **Use Structure** For any metric unit, how do you convert from milli- to centi-?

_____

19 (MP) **Use Structure** For any metric unit, how do you convert from kilo- to either gram, meter, or liter?

_____

Name _____

Solve Customary and Metric Conversion Problems

(I Can) solve problems involving conversions within the same system of measurement.

Step It Out

1 Mike observes and measures the distance a flea jumps in a straight line. If the flea jumps that same distance 8 consecutive times, how many centimeters does the flea jump?

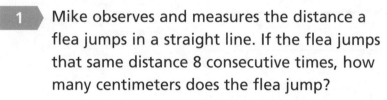 

150 millimeters

A. Find the total distance the flea jumps.

- Write an expression to find the total number of millimeters

  the flea jumps. _____

- Find the number of millimeters the flea jumps.

  _____

B. Convert the number of millimeters to a number of centimeters.

- Write an equation that relates millimeters and centimeters.

  _____

- Are you converting from a larger unit to a smaller unit or from a smaller unit to a larger unit?

  _____

- Write an expression to convert the number of millimeters the flea jumps to an equivalent number of centimeters.

  _____

C. How many centimeters does the flea jump?

  _____

 Turn and Talk How would your method change if you were converting from centimeters to millimeters?

Step It Out

2 Mike fills the aquarium using a one-pint bottle. How many times will he need to fill the bottle in order to completely fill the aquarium?

15 gallons

A. Describe how to find the number of pints the aquarium holds.

_____

_____

_____

B. Complete the table to show equivalent measures.

gallons	quarts	pints	cups
1			

C. How do you convert a number of gallons to a number of pints? Explain how you know.

_____

_____

_____

_____

D. Write an equation to show how many pints there are in 15 gallons.

_____

E. How many times will Mike need to fill the bottle in order to completely fill the aquarium?

_____

 Turn and Talk If Mike used a one-cup container to fill the aquarium instead, how would the conversion change?

Check Understanding

1 Another animal fact Mike learns is that African bush elephants eat 230 kilograms of grass and leaves each day. How many grams of grass and leaves do African bush elephants eat daily?

_____

Convert.

2 $2\frac{1}{2}$ lb to oz

3 272 mL to L

4 38.625 g to mg

_____

On Your Own

5 A large bowl has a liquid volume of $3\frac{1}{2}$ quarts. Javier fills the bowl using a 2-cup bottle. How many times will he need

to fill the bottle in order to completely fill the bowl? _____

Convert.

6 396.5 cg to g

7 13 c to qt

8 27.385 m to mm

_____

9 (MP) **Attend to Precision** A bag of nut and seed mix contains 6,250 milligrams of protein in each serving. How many grams of protein are in the whole bag?

• How many milligrams of protein are in the whole bag?

_____

• How will you convert from milligrams to grams?

_____

• How many grams of protein are in the whole bag?

_____

On Your Own

10 **STEM** A supersonic parachute will help scientists to land a spacecraft on Mars. The parachute will have to sustain a speed of 200 miles in one minute! How many yards is this in one minute?

_____

11 A striped dolphin weighs about $22\frac{1}{2}$ pounds at birth. About how many ounces does a baby striped dolphin weigh?

- Are you converting from a smaller unit to a larger unit or from a larger unit to a smaller unit?

_____

- How will you convert a number of pounds to a number of ounces? _____

- About how many ounces does a baby striped dolphin weigh? _____

12 **(MP) Reason** When you convert a measurement of 35 to an equivalent measure of 0.35, are you converting from a smaller unit to a larger unit or from a larger unit to a smaller unit? Explain.

_____

_____

_____

13 **(MP) Reason** When converting a decimal measure from a smaller metric unit to a larger metric unit, will the new measure also be a decimal? Explain.

_____

_____

_____

_____

Solve Multistep Measurement Problems

(I Can) solve a multistep problem that includes measurement conversions.

Step It Out

1 Brine is used to marinate a turkey before cooking. To make the brine, 16 cups of water are boiled with spices. After boiling, half of the original water is left. Another 3 quarts of water are added before pouring the mixture over the turkey.

How many gallons of brine are poured over the turkey?

A. First, find the amount of water that is left after boiling.

16 cups ◯ _____ = _____

B. Add the additional 3 quarts of water to the brine. How many quarts of brine are there? Show your work.

_____

_____

C. Convert the number of quarts of brine to a number of gallons. Show your work.

_____

_____

D. How many gallons of brine are poured over the turkey?

_____

 Turn and Talk Describe the solution process if the direction in Part B had asked how many cups instead of how many quarts.

Step It Out

2 Before the turkey is put in the oven, it is tied with twine. A length of 150 centimeters is tied around the body of the turkey. Three lengths of 160 millimeters each are used to tie the legs together and each of the two wings.

A new roll of twine has 10 meters of twine. If you use a new roll to tie the turkey, how many meters of twine are left on the roll?

A. Write an expression for the total amount of twine used to tie the turkey.

_____

B. How many centimeters of twine is this? Show your work.

_____

_____

_____

C. Write an expression for the amount of twine that remains on the roll.

_____

D. How many meters of twine are left on the roll? Show your work.

_____

_____

_____

 Turn and Talk How would you solve the problem differently if you were asked to find the number of centimeters of twine left on the roll?

Check Understanding

1 A brining recipe calls for 475 milliliters of water for every 2 kilograms of turkey. If a turkey weighs 8 kilograms,

how many liters of water are needed? _____

2 Sammi walks from the picnic area to the lake and back. The distance from the picnic area to the lake is 1.3 kilometers. When she gets to the lake, she walks around the lake 3 times. The distance around the lake is 685 meters. How

many kilometers does Sammi walk? _____

On Your Own

3 (MP) **Reason** Paula has several cartons of milk. She has 2 one-cup cartons, 1 one-pint carton, and 3 one-quart cartons. Will Paula be able to use her cartons of milk to completely fill a one-gallon jug? Explain.

_____

_____

4 Shelby is learning how to steer a remote-control car. On her first try, the car travels 27 inches before hitting the wall. On her second try, it travels $6\frac{3}{4}$ feet. On her third try, it travels $3\frac{1}{2}$ yards before it reaches the other side of the room. How many yards does the car travel in the three tries?

_____

5 Linda's hair was $\frac{2}{3}$ yard long before she had it cut. She had 3 inches cut off. How many feet long was Linda's hair after she had it cut?

_____

On Your Own

6 **STEM** The first computer, called the Electronic Numerical Integrator and Calculator (ENIAC), had a mass of about 27,200 kilograms. The mass of a certain model of smartphone is about 150 grams. Which has the greater mass, ENIAC or 200,000 smartphones? By how many kilograms?

_____

7 **(MP) Model with Mathematics** For an experiment, Ashok pours 0.3 liter of water into a container. He adds 50 milliliters of vegetable oil and 25 milliliters of colored detergent. How many times as much water than vegetable oil and detergent does Ashok use?

- Write an equation to show the number of milliliters of water

  Ashok uses. _____

- Write an equation to show the number of milliliters of

  vegetable oil and detergent Ashok uses. _____

- How many times as much water as vegetable oil and

  detergent does Ashok use? _____

8 **(MP) Use Structure** Lamar subtracts 100 meters from 1 kilometer. He writes the difference as a single digit followed by a unit of

measurement. What digit and unit does he use? _____

9 **(MP) Attend to Precision** Danielle frames a square picture. She has $\frac{7}{8}$ yard of wood trim left over. How many feet of wood trim did Danielle have when she started? Explain.

20.125 in.

_____

_____

_____

_____

Name _____

Concepts and Skills

1 A block of wood has a mass of 45,000 milligrams. How many

grams is this? _____

2 (MP) **Use Tools** Complete the table. Tell what strategy or tool you will use to complete the table, explain your choice, and then find the answers.

gallons	quarts	pints	cups
$2\frac{1}{8}$			

_____

_____

3 How do you convert a number of liters to a number of milliliters?

(A) Multiply by 1,000. (C) Divide by 1,000.

(B) Multiply by 100. (D) Divide by 100.

4 How would you explain to someone how to convert 324.8 ounces to pounds? Then find the number of pounds.

_____

_____

5 Select all the conversions that can be made by dividing by a whole number.

(A) quarts to cups (D) pounds to ounces

(B) inches to yards (E) kilometers to meters

(C) centigrams to grams

6 A package is secured with ribbon. Two pieces of ribbon, each measuring 1.25 meters, are wrapped around the package. A third piece of ribbon is also measured to be 1.25 meters with an extra 120 millimeters to allow for attaching a card. How many centimeters of ribbon are used?

_____

7 The distance from the park to the grocery store is 2 miles 200 yards. Complete the table for this distance in yards, feet, and inches.

Distance from Park to Store		
in yards	in feet	in inches

8 A full 5-gallon barrel of water is leaking 3 fluid ounces each day. How many quarts of water are left in the barrel after 8 days?

- (A) $3\frac{3}{4}$ quarts
- (B) $19\frac{1}{4}$ quarts
- (C) 77 quarts
- (D) 616 quarts

9 Select all the distances that are equal to 65 meters.

- (A) 0.065 kilometer
- (B) 0.65 kilometer
- (C) 650 centimeters
- (D) 6,500 centimeters
- (E) 6,500 millimeters

Unit 8

Graphs, Patterns, and Geometry

Event Planner

Event planners make events happen. They meet with clients to understand their needs. Event planners need to make many decisions. They gather information, determine what is important to the client, and work within a budget before making decisions about how to meet the client's goals.

Event planners get bids from providers, find the space for the event, and coordinate with hotels, transportation, and food services to make special occasions go smoothly.

There are many important decisions that event planners at the White House must make. They must honor the traditions and cultures of the leaders from other countries when planning formal parties that include dancing and dinner.

STEM Task:

You can make interesting patterns with just one simple shape. Draw 25 five-by-five squares on grid paper. Then draw a diagonal line from corner to corner in each of the 25 squares. Next, color half of each square black. Now cut out the 25 squares and make an interesting pattern with them. Then rearrange and make a new pattern. As you do this, share your patterns with classmates and view theirs. When you find the pattern you like best, tape or paste it onto a sheet of construction paper.

Learning Mindset
Challenge-Seeking Makes Decisions

To make decisions it is helpful to have a process. For example, you might gather information, determine what is important, and weigh that information against your goals. Making a decision about a task can involve experimenting with different outcomes as you did when you were making a design with your squares. Many things can influence a decision when working on a task, such as the availability of materials, time constraints, or expense. Using the information you gathered will help you make better decisions.

Reflect

Q What decisions did you make when you were making a pattern?

Q How did rearranging the squares help you see new possibilities?

19 Graphs and Patterns

Where is the treasure?

A treasure is hidden under a number on the hundreds chart. Use the clues to shade the other 99 numbers. The number that is left unshaded holds the treasure.

- Shade the numbers in the patterns described below.

    A. Start at 3. The rule is: Subtract 2, and then add 5.

    B. Start at 2. The rule is: Add 6.

    C. Start at 5. The rule is: Add 12.

    D. Start at 83. The rule is: Subtract 12.

    E. Start at 1. The rule is: Add 3.

1	2	3	4	5	6	7	8	9	10
11	12	13	14	15	16	17	18	19	20
21	22	23	24	25	26	27	28	29	30
31	32	33	34	35	36	37	38	39	40
41	42	43	44	45	46	47	48	49	50
51	52	53	54	55	56	57	58	59	60
61	62	63	64	65	66	67	68	69	70
71	72	73	74	75	76	77	78	79	80
81	82	83	84	85	86	87	88	89	90
91	92	93	94	95	96	97	98	99	100

The treasure is hidden under _____.

 Turn and Talk

- What patterns did you notice as you shaded in the numbers on the chart?

Are You Ready?

Complete these problems to review prior concepts and skills
you will need for this module.

Make Line Plots to Display Measurement Data

Make a line plot to show the data.

1 Jenny uses a ruler to measure the thicknesses of 12 photo albums.
The thicknesses are:

1 inch	$2\frac{1}{4}$ inches	$2\frac{1}{4}$ inches	2 inches
$1\frac{1}{2}$ inches	$2\frac{1}{4}$ inches	$2\frac{1}{2}$ inches	2 inches
$2\frac{1}{2}$ inches	$1\frac{1}{2}$ inches	$2\frac{1}{4}$ inches	$1\frac{1}{2}$ inches

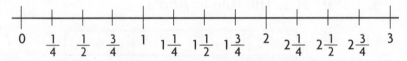

Thickness of Photo Album (in Inches)

Generate and Analyze Number Patterns

**Use the rule to write the numbers in the pattern. Then describe
another pattern in the numbers.**

2 Rule: Add 6.   First term: 2

2, _____, _____, _____, _____, _____, _____, _____

_____

3 Rule: Multiply by 2, and then add 1.   First term: 1

1, _____, _____, _____, _____, _____, _____, _____

_____

Name

Describe a Coordinate System

(I Can) identify and describe a point in a coordinate system.

Spark Your Learning

Ann lives 3 blocks east and 5 blocks north of the elementary school. Ben lives 6 blocks east and 3 blocks north of the elementary school. What directions should Ann and Ben use to walk to each other's home?

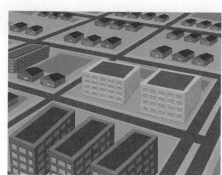

Use the grid to justify your answer.

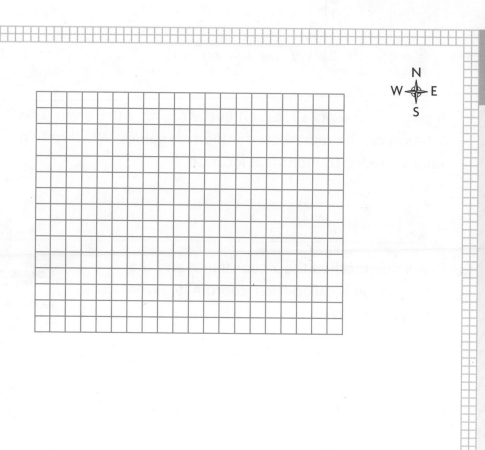

Turn and Talk Compare the directions that each person uses to get from one home to the other, and explain the differences between them.

Build Understanding

© Houghton Mifflin Harcourt Publishing Company

1 A **coordinate system** is a plane formed by two perpendicular number lines that intersect. These number lines, or **axes**, meet at 0 on each number line. This location is called the **origin**.

A. Label each axis. Label and circle the origin in the coordinate system.

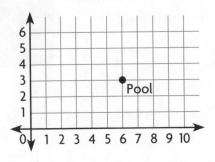

B. A point represents a location in the coordinate system. This location can be represented using two values. Why are two values needed to identify a location?

_____

_____

C. One value is called the x-coordinate and the second value is called the y-coordinate. What does each value describe?

_____

_____

_____

D. Locate the pool in the coordinate system.
What is its x-coordinate? _____

What is its y-coordinate? _____

 Turn and Talk How far from the x-axis is the pool? How far from the y-axis is the pool?

2 A city planner uses a coordinate grid to show different locations. Each unit represents one town block. What ordered pair represents the location of the pet store?

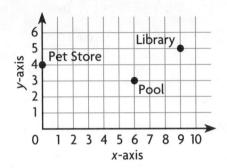

Connect to Vocabulary

A pair of numbers in the form (x, y) is called an **ordered pair**, where x represents the x-coordinate and y represents the y-coordinate. A **coordinate grid** describes all of the ordered pairs on or above the x-axis and on or to the right of the y-axis within a coordinate system.

A. How can you describe the location of the pet store?

_____

_____

B. From the origin, how do you move along each axis to

reach the pet store? _____

_____

C. At what x-coordinate is the pet store? _____

At what y-coordinate is the pet store? _____

D. What is the ordered pair that
gives the location of the pet store? _____

 Turn and Talk Could the coordinates of the ordered pair for the pet store be switched? Explain.

Check Understanding

Use the coordinate grid to answer the questions.

1 How do you move from the origin to reach the library?

_____

2 What is the ordered pair for the library?

_____

© Houghton Mifflin Harcourt Publishing Company

On Your Own

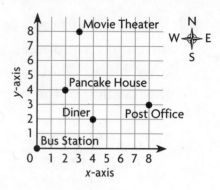

3 (MP) **Use Tools** A new cell phone app shows locations in town on a map. Each unit on the map represents one block in the town.

- What are two ways to name the location of the bus station on the map?

  _____

- Explain how the coordinates of the post office and the movie theater differ.

  _____

  _____

Describe how to move from the origin of a coordinate grid to locate the point.

4 A(7, 4)   **5** B(5, 0)   **6** C(3, 6)

_____   _____   _____

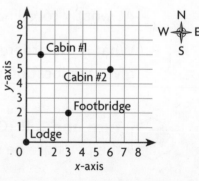

7 (MP) **Use Structure** Micah is at a lodge in the forest. He uses a map where each unit represents 100 yards.

- What ordered pair represents the location

  of the footbridge? _____

- From the lodge, how far east and how far north is Cabin #2? What is its ordered pair?

  _____

I'm in a Learning Mindset!

How am I able to help others understand ordered pairs?

_____

Name _____

Understand Ordered Pairs

(**I Can**) graph a point on a coordinate grid and interpret the coordinate values.

Spark Your Learning

The map shows the location of two buildings. Each unit represents one block.

Andi is at the art museum and Karl is at the history museum. They agree to meet at the library. The library is at the intersection of a street that is 3 blocks south of the art museum and a street that is 5 blocks west of the history museum. Who walks farther to get to the library?

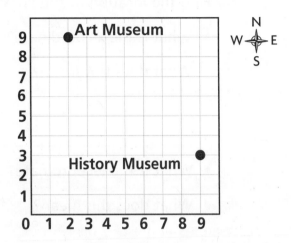

Justify your thinking.

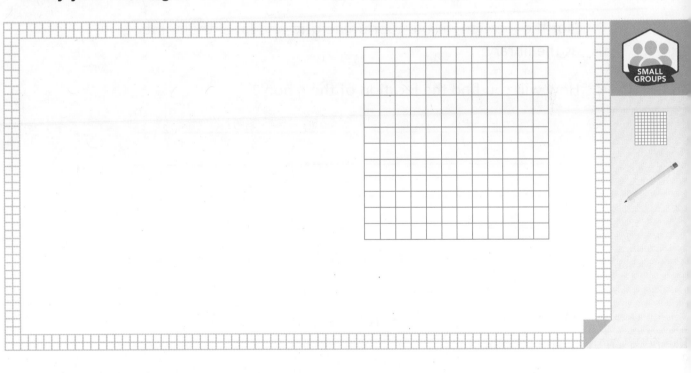

Turn and Talk Is there a point where the streets intersect so Karl and Andi walk the same number of whole blocks to meet? Explain how you know.

© Houghton Mifflin Harcourt Publishing Company

Build Understanding

1 Each unit on the map represents one block. The library is located at (6, 5). The school is located at (2, 7). Where is each building located on the map?

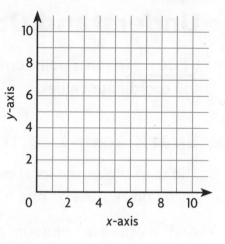

A. Find the location of the library.

- What is the *x*-coordinate? _____

- What does this mean?

_____

_____

- What is the *y*-coordinate? _____

- What does this mean?

_____

_____

B. Plot the location on the coordinate grid and label the point as the library.

C. How will you find the location of the school?

_____

_____

_____

_____

_____

D. Plot the location on the coordinate grid and label the point as the school.

 Turn and Talk Would the locations of the school and library be the same if the coordinates were (5, 6) and (7, 2)? Explain your answer.

Step It Out

2 Each unit on the map represents 1 mile.

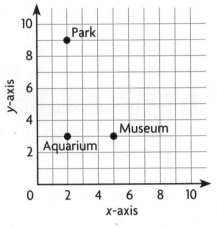

A. How far is the museum from the aquarium?

- How far from the
  y-axis is the aquarium? _____

- How far from the
  y-axis is the museum? _____

- How much farther from the *y*-axis is
  the museum compared to the aquarium? _____

- How far is the museum from the aquarium? _____

B. How far is the park from the aquarium?

- How far from the *x*-axis is the aquarium? _____

- How far from the *x*-axis is the park? _____

- How much farther from the *x*-axis is
  the park compared to the aquarium? _____

- How far is the park from the aquarium? _____

 Turn and Talk How can you use the *x*- and *y*-coordinates to
find the distances between the locations?

- -

Check Understanding Math Board

Each unit on the coordinate grid represents 1 mile.

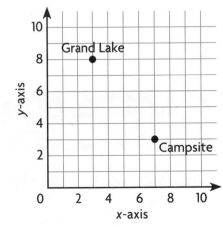

1 Mystic Falls is located at (7, 8). Plot Mystic Falls on
the coordinate grid.

2 How far is Mystic Falls from Grand Lake? _____

3 How far is Mystic Falls from the campsite? _____

On Your Own

Each unit on the coordinate grid represents 1 mile. Use the coordinate grid for 4–6.

4 (MP) **Reason** The ranch is located at (1, 9). Plot and label the location of the ranch. Explain how you plotted the point.

_____

_____

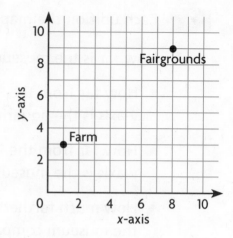

5 How far is the ranch from the farm? _____

6 How far is the ranch from the fairgrounds? _____

Plot the point on the coordinate grid.

7 A(5, 0)   **8** B(0, 4)   **9** C(8, 8)

10 D(3, 6)   **11** E(6, 3)   **12** F(9, 2)

Find the distance between the pair of points.

13 (3, 10) and (8, 10) _____

14 (8, 5) and (0, 5) _____

15 (1, 7) and (9, 7) _____

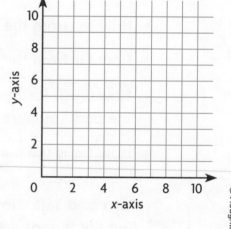

16 **Open Ended** Write a problem using ordered pairs to find the distance between two points so that the distance is 7 units.

_____

_____

I'm in a Learning Mindset!

How am I using what I know to plot points?

_____

© Houghton Mifflin Harcourt Publishing Company

Name _____

Use Ordered Pairs to Represent Problems

(I Can) use coordinate graphing to represent and solve problems.

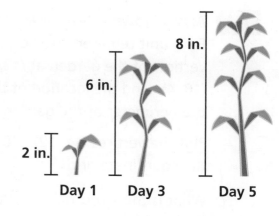

Day 1   Day 3   Day 5

Step It Out

1 Alyssa records the height of her corn plant over several days on the graph.

A. What does the point (8, 10) represent on the graph?

- What is represented along the *x*-axis?

  _____

- What is represented along the *y*-axis?

  _____

- The point (8, 10) shows that on Day _____

  the height of the corn plant is _____ inches .

B. On what day is the height of the plant 6 inches?

  _____

C. Suppose the title of the graph is changed to "Number of Servings of Corn Alyssa Eats Each Week."

- Describe how the labels would change.

  _____

- What would the point (8, 10) represent?

  _____

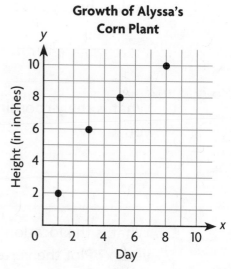

Growth of Alyssa's Corn Plant

 Turn and Talk Which point is more likely to be on Alyssa's graph, (4, 7) or (7, 4)? Explain your reasoning.

Step It Out

2 Alyssa draws a plan for a rectangular garden. Each unit represents 1 foot. She places three vertices of the garden at (12, 12), (18, 12), and (18, 4). Find the location of the fourth vertex and the perimeter of the garden.

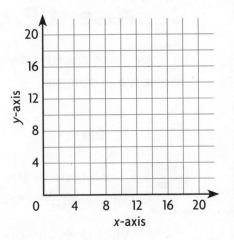

A. Plot the vertices (12, 12), (18, 12), and (18, 4) on the coordinate grid.

B. What is the x-coordinate of the fourth vertex? Explain how you know.

_____

_____

C. What is the y-coordinate of the fourth vertex? Explain how you know.

_____

_____

D. What is the location of the fourth vertex? Plot the vertex on the coordinate grid. _____

E. Subtract the x-coordinates to find the length of each horizontal side.

_____

F. Subtract the y-coordinates to find the length of each vertical side.

_____

G. What is the perimeter of the garden? Show your work.

_____

 Turn and Talk What is the area of the garden? Compare your method for finding the area with the method used by a classmate.

Name _____

Check Understanding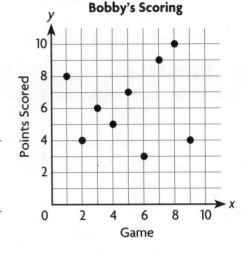

Use the graph for 1–3.

1 What could the graph represent?

_____

2 What does the point (7, 9) represent?

_____

3 During which games did
Bobby score exactly 4 points? _____

4 Three vertices of a rectangle are (1, 3), (1, 7), and (6, 7).

- What are the coordinates of the fourth vertex? _____

- What is the perimeter of the rectangle? _____

On Your Own

Use the graph for 5–7.

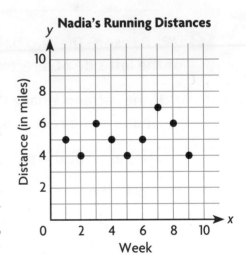

5 What could the graph represent?

_____

_____

6 What does the point (2, 4) represent?

_____

7 During which weeks did Nadia run exactly 5 miles?

_____

8 Three vertices of a rectangle are (6, 1), (3, 1), and (3, 8).

- What are the coordinates of the fourth vertex? _____

- What is the perimeter of the rectangle? _____

On Your Own

Use the graph for 9 and 10.

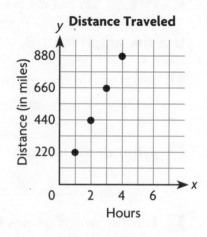

9 **STEM** One of Europe's fastest trains is remarkable because its parts are nearly all renewable and sustainable. The coordinate grid shows how far the train can travel in a number of hours. What does the point (3, 660) represent?

_____

_____

10 (MP) **Reason** Suppose the title of the graph is changed to "A Runner's Distance."

• How could the labels of the graph change?

_____

_____

• What would the point (3, 660) represent?

_____

11 (MP) **Reason** The two points shown are the vertices of the left side of a rectangle.

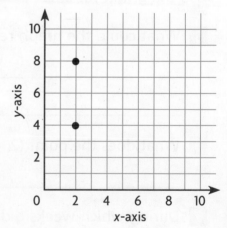

• If the rectangle has a perimeter of 20 units, what are the coordinates of the other two

vertices? Plot the points. _____

• Explain how you know.

_____

_____

_____

_____

Name _____

Generate and Identify Numerical Patterns

(I Can) use two rules to generate numerical patterns, write ordered pairs using corresponding terms, and identify a relationship between them.

Step It Out

1 ▷ Antonia and Connor are playing a patterns game. Each draws a card and finds the first five numbers in the pattern. Then they try to find a relationship between the corresponding numbers in both patterns.

Antonia's Card

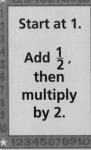
Connor's Card

A. Complete the table.

Position in Pattern	1	2	3	4	5
Antonia's Numbers	2				
Connor's Numbers	1				

B. Write the first five ordered pairs with the *x*-coordinate representing the numbers in Antonia's pattern and the *y*-coordinate representing the corresponding numbers in Connor's pattern.

_____

C. Does there appear to be a relationship between Antonia's numbers and Connor's numbers? If so, describe the relationship.

_____

_____

Turn and Talk How can you use Antonia's pattern to find the seventh number in Connor's pattern?

Step It Out

2 Nora and Pavel are playing a game. The game cards show either "Move forward 3." or "Move forward 6." Just by chance, Nora draws "Move forward 3." on her first three turns. Pavel draws "Move forward 6." on his first three turns.

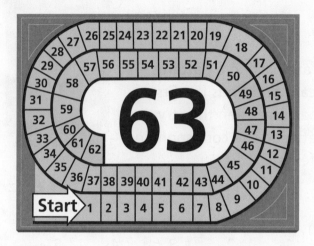

A. At what number on the game board is Nora after her first turn? Her second turn? Her third turn?

_____

B. At what number on the game board is Pavel after his first turn? His second turn? His third turn?

_____

C. Using Nora's locations as the *x*-coordinates and Pavel's locations as the *y*-coordinates, write the ordered pairs after each turn.

_____

D. Does there appear to be a relationship between Pavel's location and Nora's location? Explain.

_____

 Turn and Talk What is another way to describe the relationship between Pavel's location and Nora's location?

Check Understanding [Math Board]

1 Erin and Joshua are writing number patterns.

> **Erin:** Start at 1; rule: "Add 1, then multiply by 3."
>
> **Joshua:** Start at $\frac{1}{2}$; rule: "Add $\frac{1}{2}$, then multiply by 2."

Use the numbers in Erin's pattern for the *x*-coordinates and the numbers in Joshua's pattern for the *y*-coordinates. Write the first five ordered pairs.

_____

2 Kona and Isabella do pushups each week. On the first day, Kona does 3 pushups and follows the rule "Add 3" for the number of pushups on the following days. Isabella does 1 pushup and follows the rule "Add 1" for the number of pushups on the following days. They follow their patterns for 5 days.

- How many pushups does Kona do on each day?

_____

- How many pushups does Isabella do on each day?

_____

- Write the ordered pairs for the corresponding numbers of pushups, using Isabella's numbers for the *x*-coordinates and Kona's numbers for the *y*-coordinates.

_____

- Does there appear to be a relationship between the number of pushups Kona does and the number of pushups Isabella does? If so, describe the relationship.

_____

_____

_____

On Your Own

3 Zach and Eliza are writing number patterns. Zach starts with 1 and uses the rule "Multiply by 2, then add 1." Eliza starts with 2 and uses the rule "Add 1, then multiply by 2."

- Write the first five ordered pairs with the x-coordinate representing the numbers in Zach's pattern and the y-coordinate representing the corresponding numbers in Eliza's pattern.

- What appears to be the relationship between Zach's numbers and Eliza's numbers?

4 (MP) **Reason** Quentin's hair grows $\frac{3}{2}$ centimeters every month and Maurice's hair grows 1 centimeter every month. On haircut day, the length of Maurice's hair and Quentin's hair is 2 centimeters. The boys do not get another haircut for 4 months.

- Complete the table to show the length in centimeters of each boy's hair.

Number of Months After Haircut	0	1	2	3	4
Quentin's Hair Length (in cm)	2				
Maurice's Hair Length (in cm)	2				

- Find the difference in the lengths of the boys' hair each month.

- Does there appear to be a relationship in the monthly differences? If so, what is the relationship?

Name _____

Identify and Graph Relationships and Patterns

(I Can) write and graph ordered pairs on a coordinate grid using two numerical patterns.

Step It Out

1 In math class, Fernando learns that the rule "Add 1" to the side length of a triangle with equal side lengths results in the rule "Add 3" to the perimeter.

A. Write the values generated by these rules in the table.

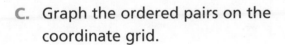

Side Length (in inches)	0	1			
Perimeter (in inches)	0	3			

B. Use the values in the table to write ordered pairs that relate the side length to the corresponding perimeter.

_____

C. Graph the ordered pairs on the coordinate grid.

D. How does the perimeter relate to side length?

_____

_____

_____

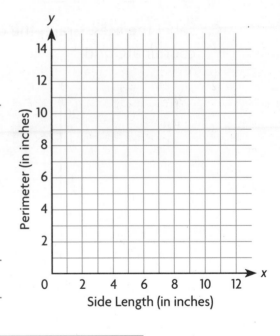

Turn and Talk What are some other ordered pairs that could fit the pattern? How do you know?

Step It Out

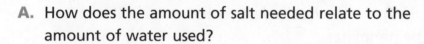

2 A science class uses salt and water to make a saltwater battery. The table shows the amount of salt needed for the amount of water used.

Water (in cups)	0	3	6	9
Salt (in teaspoons)	0	4	8	12

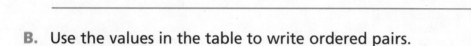

A. How does the amount of salt needed relate to the amount of water used?

_____

_____

B. Use the values in the table to write ordered pairs.

_____

C. Label the axes. Graph the ordered pairs on the coordinate grid.

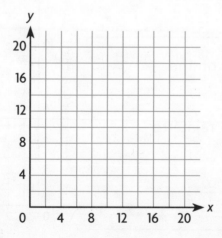

D. If the class uses 15 cups of water, how much salt does

the class need? _____

Turn and Talk If one group of students uses 2 teaspoons of salt, how much water does the group use? Explain how you know.

Name _____

Check Understanding

1. Fernando also learns in math class that the rule "Add 1" to the side length of a pentagon with equal side lengths results in the rule "Add 5" to the perimeter. Write four ordered pairs that relate the side length of a pentagon to the perimeter of the pentagon.

_____

Use the table for 2–4.

Hours Worked	0	1	2
Earnings (in dollars)	0	8	16

2. Use the values in the table to write ordered pairs.

_____

3. Graph the ordered pairs. Label the axes.

_____

4. What would be the earnings for 4 hours of work?

_____

On Your Own

5. For each person, $10 is added to the bill.

- Complete the table.

Number of People	1		
Amount of the Bill (in dollars)			

- Use the values in the table to write ordered pairs.

_____

- What would be the amount of the bill for 6 people? _____

On Your Own

6 **STEM** In an experiment, vinegar and iodine are mixed together to make a clear liquid. After 1 minute, the clear liquid changes to a dark liquid. The table shows the amount of iodine needed for the amount of vinegar used.

Vinegar (in teaspoons)	0	2	4	6
Iodine (in drops)	0	3	6	9

- Graph the ordered pairs represented in the table. Label the axes.

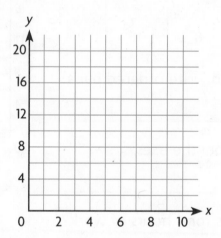

- How much iodine is needed for 10 teaspoons of vinegar?

_____

- How much vinegar is needed for 12 drops of iodine?

_____

7 **(MP)** **Use Structure** The graph shows the distance Cora walks.

- Write the ordered pairs that correspond to the points in this graph.

_____

- How is the distance Cora walks related to the amount of time she walks?

_____

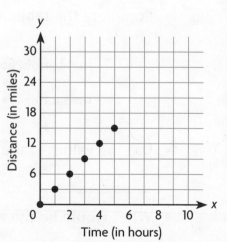

© Houghton Mifflin Harcourt Publishing Company • Image Credit: ©Houghton Mifflin Harcourt

Review

Vocabulary

1 Draw lines to match the description to the term.

the horizontal number line on a coordinate grid •   • *x*-axis

the vertical number line on a coordinate grid •   • *x*-coordinate

the first number in an ordered pair •   • *y*-axis

the second number in an ordered pair •   • *y*-coordinate

Concepts and Skills

2 Which point is located at (5, 2)?

Ⓐ point *A*

Ⓑ point *B*

Ⓒ point *C*

Ⓓ point *D*

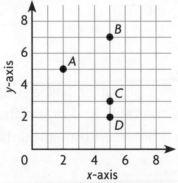

3 Three vertices of a rectangle are located at (8, 5), (6, 5), and (6, 2). Graph the rectangle. Where is the fourth vertex located? What is the perimeter?

_____

4 (MP) **Use Tools** What is the distance between the points (5, 3) and (5, 5)? Tell what strategy or tool you will use to solve the problem, explain your choice, and then find

the answer. _____

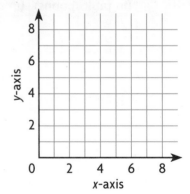

5 Point *A* has coordinates (3, 4). Point *B* is 2 units farther from the *y*-axis than point *A*. Which ordered pair represents the coordinates of point *B*?

Ⓐ (3, 2)   Ⓑ (3, 6)   Ⓒ (1, 4)   Ⓓ (5, 4)

6 In the graph, what could the point located at (6, 3) represent?

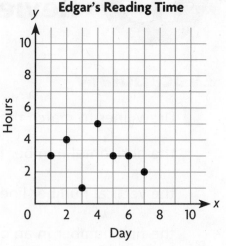

Edgar's Reading Time

_____

_____

7 Chelsea and Melissa are writing number patterns. Chelsea starts at 0 and uses the rule "Add 2, then multiply by 2." Melissa starts at 2 and uses the rule "Add 4." Select all of the ordered pairs in which the x-coordinate represents a number in Chelsea's pattern and the y-coordinate represents the corresponding number in Melissa's pattern.

Ⓐ (2, 0)　　　Ⓓ (24, 14)

Ⓑ (0, 2)　　　Ⓔ (60, 18)

Ⓒ (12, 10)

8 For every 2 tablespoons of butter, Sasha uses 3 tablespoons of flour for her sauce. Complete the table and graph the ordered pairs. What appears to be the relationship between the amounts of butter and flour?

Butter (in tablespoons)	Flour (in tablespoons)
2	3
4	6
12	

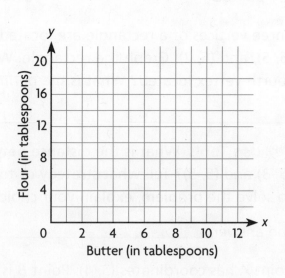

_____

_____

_____

Classify Two-Dimensional Figures

How many right triangles?

• How many right triangles can you find in

the figure? _____

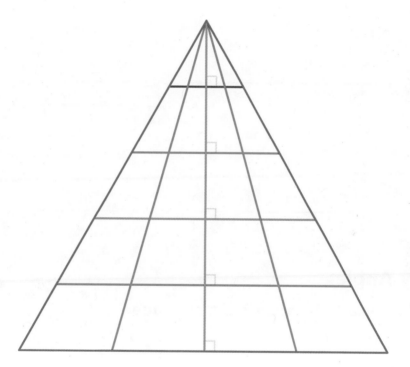

 Turn and Talk

• How did you solve the problem?

• What other types of triangles appear to be in the figure?

Are You Ready?

Complete these problems to review prior concepts and skills
you will need for this module.

Quadrilaterals

Name the shape in as many ways as possible, if a trapezoid is defined
as having exactly 1 pair of parallel sides. Write *quadrilateral*, *square*,
rectangle, *rhombus*, *trapezoid*, or *parallelogram*.

1

_____

2

_____

3

_____

4

_____

Classify Angles

Classify the angle. Write *acute*, *right*, or *obtuse*.

5

_____

6

_____

7

_____

8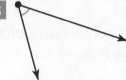

_____

Name

Identify and Classify Polygons

(I Can) identify and classify polygons.

Spark Your Learning

Many of the figures found in art, nature, and science are familiar.

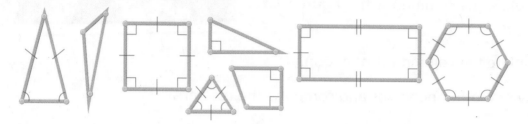

Group the polygons shown based on two or more features, or attributes, they have in common.

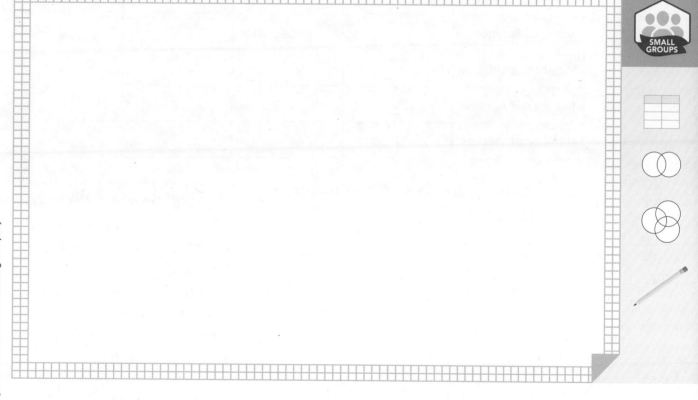

 Turn and Talk Into which of your groups would you place this polygon? Explain your reasoning.

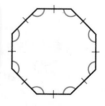

Build Understanding

1 Mr. Berger and his class are looking at the polygon shown.

A. Record the attributes of different polygons in the table.

- Complete the column for the figure that has 7 vertices.

- Complete the column for nonagon.

- Draw two other polygons and complete the columns.

Name of Polygon		nonagon		
Number of Sides				
Number of Angles				
Number of Vertices	7			

B. What do you notice about the attributes of each polygon?

_____

_____

_____

_____

Connect to Vocabulary

The prefix *hepta-* is Greek for the number 7, so a **heptagon** is a polygon with seven sides. The prefix *nona-* is Latin for the number 9, so a **nonagon** is a polygon with nine sides.

 Turn and Talk If you add one side to a polygon, how do the numbers of sides and vertices change? What if you add two sides?

2 Mr. Berger drew these polygons on a whiteboard.

Group 1   Group 2

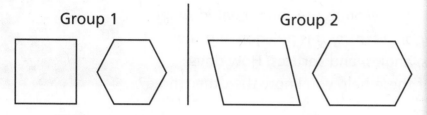

Connect to Vocabulary

The word **congruent** describes equal angle measures or equal side lengths in a figure. A **regular polygon** is a polygon in which all sides are congruent and all angles are congruent.

A. What do you notice about the attributes of the polygons in Group 1?

_____

_____

B. What do you notice about the attributes of the polygons in Group 2?

_____

_____

C. Describe both groups of polygons using the words *congruent* and *regular*.

_____

_____

_____

 Turn and Talk Draw a regular polygon and a polygon that is not regular on a separate sheet of paper. Compare and contrast your drawings with those of a classmate.

• •

Check Understanding

1 Tam is cutting pieces of stained glass for a design. How would she determine whether the figures she cuts are regular polygons or not?

_____

On Your Own

2 (MP) **Use Structure** Honeycombs use the repeated shape of one type of polygon. Identify this polygon and the numbers of its sides, angles, and vertices. How does knowing any one of these help you know the other three?

_____

_____

_____

(MP) **Use Structure** Name the polygon. Tell whether it is a *regular polygon* or *not a regular polygon* and its number of sides.

3

4

_____   _____

5 (MP) **Use Tools** Kim connects 7 of the dots on the dot paper.

- She says the figure has seven sides, so she has drawn a heptagon. Is she correct? Explain.

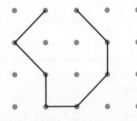

_____

_____

- Connect the dots at the top. Name the polygon and tell how many sides and angles it has.

_____

⊹ I'm in a Learning Mindset!

What would I like to learn more about when I am studying classification of polygons?

_____

© Houghton Mifflin Harcourt Publishing Company • Image Credit: ©StudioSmart/Shutterstock

Name

Classify and Organize Triangles

(I Can) classify triangles.

Spark Your Learning

The house shown is called an A-frame house. Architects use triangular shapes in many building designs.

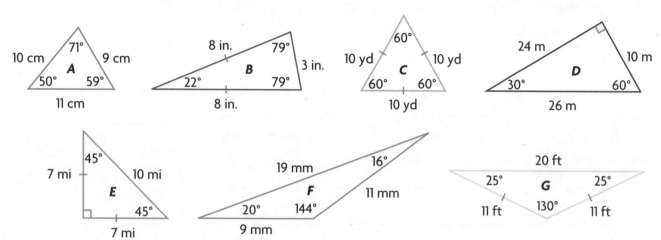

Group the triangles according to their attributes.

Turn and Talk Draw a square. Use a ruler to draw a diagonal line to form two triangles. Describe your triangles.

Build Understanding

1 The angles of the roofs on buildings can form many different types of triangles. Complete the tables by classifying the triangles by angle measures and by side lengths. Write *acute* (greater than 0° and less than 90°), *obtuse* (greater than 90° and less than 180°), *or right* (equal to 90°). Then write *isosceles, scalene,* or *equilateral.*

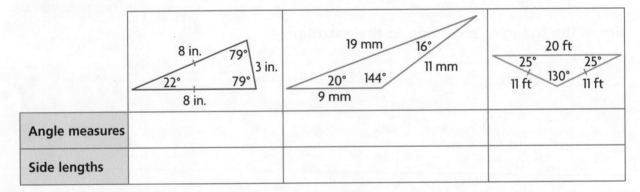

Angle measures				
Side lengths				

Angle measures			
Side lengths			

A. What do the angles of the right triangles and the obtuse triangles have in common?

_____

B. Is it possible to draw a triangle that is both obtuse and equilateral? Explain.

_____

 Turn and Talk Are equilateral triangles also isosceles triangles? Are all isosceles triangles also equilateral triangles? Explain.

Step It Out

2 Draw and name a triangle with exactly two congruent sides and all angles smaller than a right angle.

A. Name the first attribute of the triangle given. Then draw that part of the triangle.

_____

B. Name the second attribute. Then complete the drawing of the triangle.

_____

C. Classify the triangle you drew by its angles and by its sides.

_____

Check Understanding ![Math Board]

1 Each floor of the Flatiron building in New York City is shaped like a triangle. Look at this blueprint of one of the floors. Which terms best describe the shape of the floor? Explain your reasoning.

_____

_____

_____

Flatiron Building
New York City

Classify the triangle. Write _acute, obtuse_, or _right_. Then write _isosceles, scalene_, or _equilateral_.

2
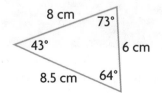
8 cm 73°
43°
6 cm
8.5 cm 64°

3 **angles:** 100°, 23°, 57°
sides: 20 yd, 8 yd, 17 yd

_____   _____

On Your Own

4 **(MP)** **Construct Arguments** Tyler
and Kiara each draw a line
segment on the same isosceles
triangle to form smaller triangles.
Are their smaller triangles
isosceles? Explain.

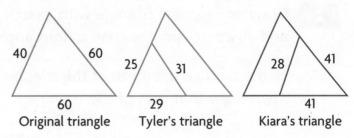

Original triangle   Tyler's triangle   Kiara's triangle

_____

_____

(MP) **Use Structure** **Classify the triangle. Write *acute, obtuse*, or *right*. Then
write *isosceles, scalene*, or *equilateral*.**

5 **angles:** 45°, 90°, 45°
   sides: 5 cm, 7 cm, 5 cm

6 **angles:** 13°, 20°, 147°
   sides: 10 ft, 15 ft, 24 ft

_____   _____

7 **(MP)** **Attend to Precision** Compare the triangles.

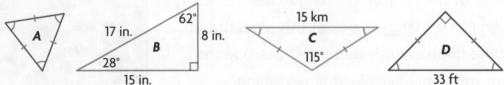

- Name one attribute that three of the triangles have in common.

_____

- Name one attribute that only one of the triangles has.

_____

⦡ I'm in a Learning Mindset!

What parts of classifying triangles am I comfortable finding on my own?

_____

Name

Classify and Organize Quadrilaterals

(I Can) classify and compare quadrilaterals.

Spark Your Learning

Farmlands, when viewed from above, often look like they are divided into different polygons, including quadrilaterals.

Look at the quadrilaterals shown. Make a list of five attributes that a quadrilateral can have. Then write the number of each quadrilateral matching each attribute.

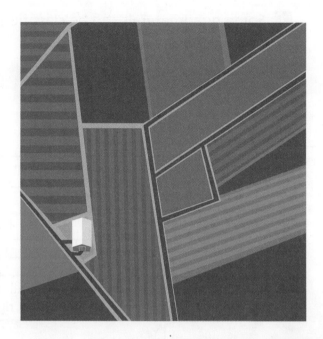

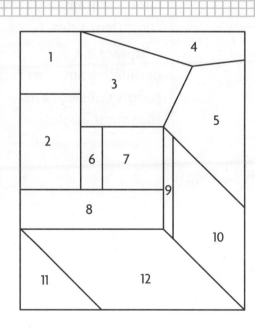

SMALL GROUPS

Turn and Talk Compare your list with the list of a classmate. Based on your attributes, how would you classify quadrilaterals?

© Houghton Mifflin Harcourt Publishing Company

Build Understanding

1 Some quadrilaterals can be classified by more than one attribute.

A. Complete the chart.

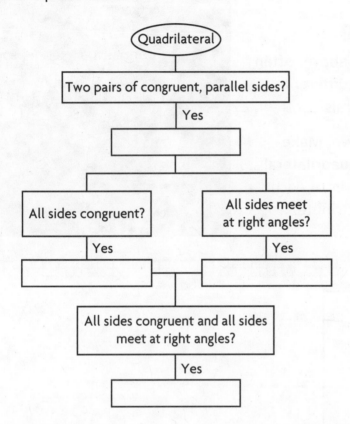

Connect to Vocabulary

A **parallelogram** is a quadrilateral with pairs of opposite sides that are congruent and parallel. Some parallelograms have special names based on their specific properties.

A **rectangle** is a parallelogram with four right angles.

A **rhombus** is a parallelogram with four congruent sides.

A **square** is a parallelogram with four congruent sides and four right angles.

B. What attributes does a square have in common with a rhombus?

_____

_____

C. What attributes does a rectangle have in common with a parallelogram?

_____

_____

 Turn and Talk What three figures have attributes in common? What are the attributes?

Step It Out

2 An artist draws a stained glass design using quadrilaterals.

A. Find and shade all the quadrilaterals among these figures in the diagram.

B. Find the trapezoids.

- Write *1* if there is **exactly one pair** of parallel sides.

- Write *2* if there is **at least one pair** of parallel sides.

C. Write *3* in each parallelogram.

D. Based on parts B and C, what attributes do parallelograms and trapezoids share under each definition of a trapezoid?

_____

_____

_____

Connect to Vocabulary

There are two accepted definitions of a trapezoid. One definition defines a **trapezoid** as having **exactly one** pair of parallel sides. The other definition defines a trapezoid as having **at least one** pair of parallel sides.

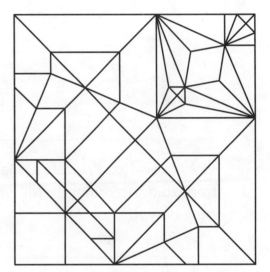

··

Check Understanding

1 Tonya defines a trapezoid as having exactly one pair of parallel sides. Which quadrilaterals are also always trapezoids by her definition? Explain.

_____

_____

Identify each statement as *true* or *false*.

2 A parallelogram is always a rhombus.

_____

3 A rhombus is always a parallelogram.

_____

4 A square is always a rhombus.

_____

5 A rectangle is always a rhombus.

_____

On Your Own

6 (MP) **Use Structure** Kent draws a quadrilateral that is a rhombus but not a square. What are its properties?

_____

_____

(MP) **Use Structure** Classify the quadrilateral in as many ways as possible. Write *quadrilateral*, *parallelogram*, *rectangle*, *rhombus*, or *square*.

7

8

9

_____   _____   _____

10 (MP) **Attend to Precision** Marylia says that a parallelogram is also a trapezoid. According to Marylia, what other shapes are also trapezoids? How do you know?

_____

_____

11 **Open Ended** Patrick defines a trapezoid as a quadrilateral with exactly one pair of parallel sides. How can he draw a line segment on this figure to make a trapezoid? Draw the segment and explain.

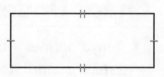

_____

🧮 I'm in a Learning Mindset!

What evidence do I have that I classified quadrilaterals correctly?

_____

Name _____

Use Venn Diagrams to Classify Two-Dimensional Figures

(**I Can**) compare and classify two-dimensional figures using Venn diagrams.

Spark Your Learning

A mosaic is a piece of artwork made with glass, stone, or ceramic tiles. Mosaic tiles come in many shapes.

Draw a Venn diagram to represent the relationships among these polygons. Explain your diagram.

SMALL GROUPS

 Turn and Talk What attributes did you use to relate the polygons in each group? Explain your reasoning.

Build Understanding

1 Lila is designing a video game in which the players arrange quadrilaterals. She defines a trapezoid as having exactly one pair of parallel sides.

A. Complete the Venn diagram to show how squares, rectangles, and rhombuses are related to parallelograms and trapezoids. Label your figures.

Quadrilaterals

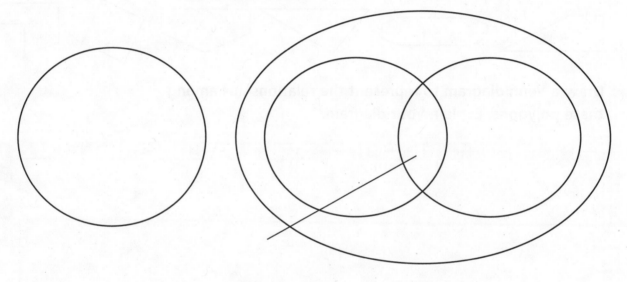

B. Explain how the diagram would change when a trapezoid is defined as a quadrilateral having at least one pair of parallel sides.

_____

_____

_____

_____

 Turn and Talk Based on your Venn diagram, how does the definition of a trapezoid affect how parallelograms and subcategories of parallelograms are classified?

Step It Out

2 Venn diagrams can be used to sort two-dimensional figures by their shared attributes. Sort the polygons into the diagram based on the categories labeled for each circle.

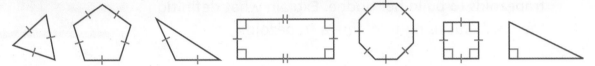

Classify the figure. Identify whether the figure:

- shares all three attributes. Draw it in the middle section where all three circles intersect.

- shares two attributes. Draw it in the section where the two circles intersect.

- shares only one attribute. Draw it in the larger section of the circle.

- <u>does not</u> share any of the attributes. Draw it outside of the circles.

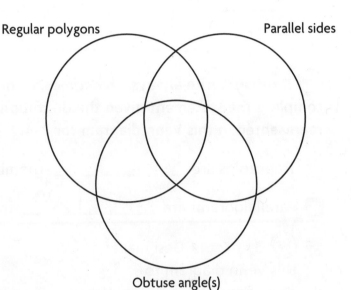

Regular polygons   Parallel sides

Obtuse angle(s)

· ·

Check Understanding [Math Board]

1 Randi made a Venn diagram where a circle representing rhombuses is inside a circle representing trapezoids. What other figures belong in the circle with the trapezoids? Explain.

_____

_____

_____

_____

On Your Own

2 (MP) **Use Structure** Gina is using blocks that are squares and trapezoids to build a bridge. Her teacher comments that she likes how Gina is using all trapezoids to build her bridge. Explain what definition the teacher is using to define a trapezoid.

_____

_____

_____

(MP) **Reason** Write *always*, *sometimes*, or *never* to complete the statement given the definition of trapezoid represented in this Venn diagram for 3–4.

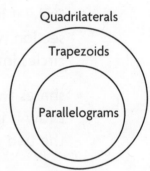

3 Trapezoids are _____ rhombuses.

4 Parallelograms are _____ trapezoids.

5 (MP) **Use Tools** Desi makes this Venn diagram to show how polygons are related.

- Label the circles for parallelograms, isosceles triangles, and regular polygons.

- Draw a square, regular pentagon, right isosceles triangle, equilateral triangle, and rhombus in the diagram.

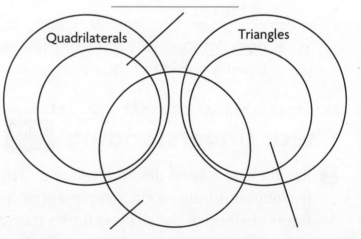

➗ I'm in a Learning Mindset!

How do I break down the task from Step It Out into smaller steps?

_____

Module 20 Review

Vocabulary

1 Write each term in the correct section of the Venn diagram.

- equilateral triangle
- isosceles triangle
- regular heptagon
- regular nonagon
- scalene triangle

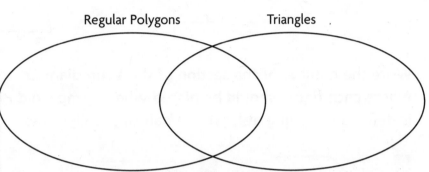

Regular Polygons   Triangles

Concepts and Skills

2 **(MP)** **Use Tools** Which statement is true? Tell what strategy or tool you will use to answer the question, explain your choice, and then find the answer.

Ⓐ All right triangles are also acute triangles.

Ⓑ All obtuse triangles are also scalene triangles.

Ⓒ All isosceles triangles are also equilateral triangles.

Ⓓ All equilateral triangles are also isosceles triangles.

_____

_____

Write *always*, *sometimes*, or *never* to make the statement true for 3–5.

3 A regular quadrilateral is _____ a square.

4 A rhombus is _____ a parallelogram.

5 A parallelogram is _____ a rectangle.

Name the polygon. Tell whether it is a *regular polygon* or *not a regular polygon* and its number of sides.

6 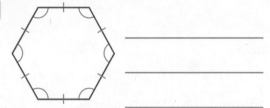 _____
_____
_____

7 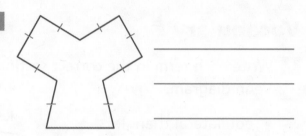 _____
_____
_____

Write the number of the section of the Venn diagram where each figure should be placed when a trapezoid is defined as having at least one pair of parallel sides.

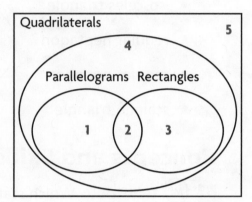

8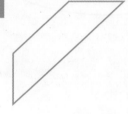

9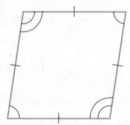

_____   _____

10 Select all the categories that always describe a figure in which all of the angles have the same measure.

Ⓐ decagon   Ⓒ regular polygon   Ⓔ hexagon

Ⓑ regular decagon   Ⓓ polygon   Ⓕ square

11 List as many attributes as possible for a figure that can be placed in the overlapping area of the Venn diagram. Name the figure.

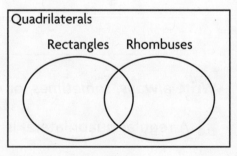

_____

_____

_____

_____

Index

N

Index

solid figures *(continued)*
  building with unit cubes, 95–98, 99–102
  dimensions, 107–112
  volume, 103–106, 108–112, 113–116, 117–122

square, 506–508, 509–512

STEM Task, 1, 125, 144, 177, 235, 315, 365, 415, 458, 469

subtraction
  of decimals, 343–346, 348–350, 355–358, 359–362
  of fractions, 130–132, 137–140, 149–152, 153–156
  of mixed numbers, 157–160, 161–166, 171–174
  reasonableness of differences, 153–156, 157–160, 172, 347–350

sum. *See also* addition
  estimate, 149–152
  reasonableness of, 153–156, 157–160, 171, 347–350

T

Table of Measures. *See More Practice and Homework Journal*

technology and digital resources. *See* Ed: Your Friend in Learning for interactive instruction, interactive practice, and videos.

thousandths, 319–322, 323–326, 327–330, 331–334

three-dimensional figures. *See* solid figures (three-dimensional figures)

time, 309–312

ton (T), 297, 299

trapezoid, 507, 508, 510, 511, 512

triangle, 501–504, 509–512

two-dimensional figures
  classify, 509–512
  polygon, 497–500
  quadrilateral, 505–508
  triangle, 501–504

U

unit cube, 95–98, 99–102, 107–112

unit fractions
  division with, 243–246, 247–252, 253–256, 257–262, 267–270, 271–274, 275–278, 279–282, 283–286, 287–290
  multiplication with, 191–194

unlike denominator, 141–144, 153–156, 157–160, 161–166, 167–170, 171–174

V

Venn diagram, 509–512

vertex, 482–484, 493, 498, 500

volume
  of composed figures, 117–122
  defined, 100
  dimensions and, 107–112
  estimate, 103–106
  formulas for, 113–116
  unit cubes and, 95–98, 99–102, 107–112

W

week (wk), 309–312

weight conversions, 297–299, 303–304, 306–307, 461–462

whole numbers
  division
    decimals and, 425–428, 433–436
    by fractions, 253–256, 257–262, 271–274, 275–278, 287–290
    fractions by, 243–246, 247–252, 279–282, 283–286, 288–290
  multiplication
    decimals and, 370, 372–374, 375–378, 379–382, 383–388, 389–392, 393–396
    fractions and, 185–190, 209–212
    of multi-digit numbers, 21–24, 25–28

word form, 10–12, 325